EAT TO
THRIVE

THE ANTI-DIET COOKBOOK

EAT TO THRIVE

THE ANTI-DIET COOKBOOK

STOP DIETING AND START LIVING WITH
50 MOUTH-WATERING RECIPES YOU
CAN MAKE IN 30 MINUTES OR LESS!

BY KATIE SAMPAYO

THIS BOOK PRESENTS THE RESEARCH AND IDEAS OF ITS AUTHOR. IT IS NOT INTENDED TO BE A SUBSTITUTE FOR CONSULTATION WITH A PROFESSIONAL HEALTHCARE PRACTITIONER. CONSULT WITH YOUR HEALTHCARE PRACTITIONER BEFORE MAKING ANY DIETARY CHANGES TO YOUR EATING HABITS OR SUPPLEMENT REGIMEN. THE PUBLISHER AND AUTHOR DISCLAIM RESPONSIBILITY FOR ANY ADVERSE EFFECTS RESULTING DIRECTLY OR INDIRECTLY FROM INFORMATION CONTAINED IN THIS BOOK.

Copyright © 2018 by Live to Thrive, LLC
All rights reserved.

Food Photography by Julie Fisher
Cover Photography by Julie Hove Andersen
Food Styling by Chara-Rontouli-Bacher
Design by Alexa B. Creative & Design
Production by PCA

www.katiesampayo.com

NOT FOR RESALE

This book is published by Live to Thrive, LLC. All rights reserved. No part of this book may be reproduced in any manner whatsoever without written permission from the publisher, except for the inclusion of brief quotations in a review. For information about permission to reproduce selections from this book, write to info@katiesampayo.com.

ISBN: 978-0-692-85586-7

FOR ANYONE WHO HAS DIETED, BUT
WAS NOT SATISFIED... SELF-LOVE,
TRUE HAPPINESS, AND A THRIVING
LIFE IS YET TO COME.

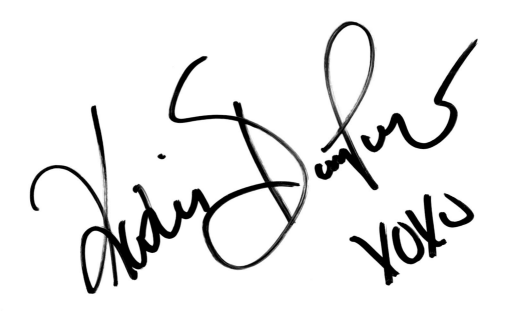

CONTENTS

INTRODUCTION
Stop Dieting. Start Living.

So this is an anti-diet cookbook. Sounds cool, right? I think so too, and I'm a personal trainer who hates the word "diet." Before I get into why I hate that word, let's get to know each other. After all, if you follow the advice I'm going to offer you, we're going to get pretty close. So let's not mess around, and get right to becoming friends.

LET'S BE REAL: DIETS SUCK.

You know it because you bought this book; I know it because I wrote it. You tried those "fad" diets and found they're a waste of time, energy, and money. They leave you feeling like you took one step forward and two steps back. I mean, who the hell can eat 1200 calories a day and somehow still have enough juice to have a kick-ass workout without keeling over mid-stride? People who, in my opinion, aren't practicing what they preach, because they're preaching the impossible.

Beyond that, these fad diets come and go like ice cream flavors of the month. Remember the Atkins diet craze a few years ago? We eliminate all carbs from our diets and instead stuff enough red meat down our throats to keep a small ranch in business? Great idea. Carbs aren't the devil, like most women tend to think. Saturated fat and cholesterol are the devil, and red meat is jam-packed with both.

Good lord, diets. Remember the fat-free one? "Fat-free" cheese, cake, and even pizza was the norm. Fat-free foods are not only completely disgusting, but they're loaded with sugar to make up for the taste. Your body turns that sugar pretty much directly into fat, so you can say so long to that six pack.

Oh yeah, and those infamous juice "cleanses" everyone loves. 6 juices a day for 3–10 days, and if you're lucky, you're allowed to have one delicious low-calorie "snack pack." It must be safe, since it's in pretty glass bottles and celebrities are doing it, right? Just like everything else celebrities buy in small glass bottles, WRONG. I'm not sure when someone decided that "healthy detox" meant "starve yourself for days," but here we are, talking about this.

The world today is a misleading place, filled with "diets" that can deprive your body of vital nutrients, and make you hate yourself even more than you did before you realized you needed this book. You know this, since you've tried a few yourself. You're over it, and you want something that actually works. Well, here you are.

THIS IS THE NO-NONSENSE, STRAIGHT TALK GUIDE TO TAKING ON YOUR BODY AND YOUR LIFE.

THE NO-NONSENSE TRUTH ABOUT DIETS

So you want to get healthy, eat right, feel great, and look damn good in a bikini. Yet you've seen yourself in the mirror in the thick of a "diet," and you're still unsatisfied. Clearly the diet route isn't working, so what can?

Well, this is probably the first little, yet extremely important, tweak I suggest you start grinding into your skull. Mind-Blowing Secret No. 1: Understand that food made in a factory probably has gross-ass factory stuff crammed into it, and your body doesn't really need to give all that extra effort required to de-process that processed crap. Eating food that came out of some conveyor belt and not the earth is like buying a knock-off cashmere sweater. And you're freaking made of cashmere, aren't you?

Beyond the healthy lifestyle, you want those toned arms and legs. Mind-Blowing Secret No. 2: If you get off your butt and move around a few days a week, you're already on your way. The concept is pretty simple. *However, if it's so simple, why isn't everyone doing it, and more importantly, why aren't you?* To be fair, you probably started your last "healthy diet" strong, meal prepping and easing off those cheese-loaded sandwiches. Then before you knew it, you were beginning to wonder if fainting at your desk was supposed to be normal. Plus, happy hours are more fun than the elliptical. Life happens, and another "diet" bites the dust.

So you've tried all this before. Eating a big juicy burger with fries is bad; eating a spinach salad with grilled chicken is good. Sitting on the couch is bad; going to the gym is good. But you've done those good things, and your results haven't been as good as you wanted. Your body and life didn't change, nor did the boring view from the elliptical. So you want more. *You want a plan that works.*

Three years ago, I was in the same place as you are now. I got to where I am today because I did something about it. I decided that I didn't want to settle for less, and I'm sure you feel the same.

The funny thing is, I've never "dieted." Simply, I realized early on that thinking about food under the guise of "dieting" isn't the healthy way to approach food at all. Dieting triggers your mind to think: *"Cut down," "Reduce," "Starve," and so on.* This sounds pretty miserable, right? So why put yourself through it? Don't; there's a better way. I'll show you how…

HOW YOU'RE GOING TO THRIVE WITHOUT A DIET

Tell me if this sounds familiar: *wake up; grab a granola bar for breakfast; run out the door to head to mind-numbing job; work 8 hours without moving from a dungeon-like cubicle; rush to the gym to make 6:00 PM body pump class; suffer for 60 minutes; go home around 7:30 PM; microwave a three-minute, processed frozen meal; do it all again the next day.*

But sometimes I'd try to spice it up too. Sometimes I would attempt to mix up my routine by swapping my granola bar for a yogurt. Sometimes instead of going to a cardio pumping fitness class, I would hit up the elliptical for 45 minutes and do some abs. I was living the life, I loved my body, and everything was perfect. Right…

Well… I mean, I felt okay…

NOTHING WAS TERRIBLE IN MY LIFE; EVERYTHING WAS GENERALLY "OK."

Then one day I woke up and finally had enough with just being "OK." At that exact moment, I committed to making a change, so much so, that I've spent the past three years of my life working on becoming the most amazing, confident, happy, healthy, fit, and fulfilled version of myself. I know, a mouthful right? It's worth saying every time though, and I now love myself and my life. All it took was a few little tweaks and adjustments that I'd like to share with you.

These past three years helped me find a great place; this book will help you find one too. "OK" isn't OK in this place; in this place, you are genuinely excited about life, your body, and yourself. Not to mention the non-diet food you're putting into your mouth.

COMMITMENT LEADS TO SUCCESS

So, we said this is an anti-diet cookbook. It sounds like a simple concept, right? Well, really, it really, really is that simple. All it takes are small, easy changes to your eating habits by thinking outside the box when it comes to nutrition. No more diets. No more "quick" fixes. Eliminate these words from your vocabulary now, and never say them again.

But before we move forward, a few commitments need to be established. You need to actually read this book, not just flip to the recipes and call it a day. If you do that, you will miss everything, and this book will just be another dusty item on your bookshelf (or hard drive). You will also continue to stay exactly where you are right now; "OK." Maybe that's what you want, but most likely not. You want more than an "OK" body; you want to never try another "diet" again; and you want to thrive.

So pay attention to what you're about to read and put what you learn into action. Knowledge is the key to power, and I'm giving this power to you on a silver platter. Worst-case scenario, after reading this book, you'll have a wealth of super interesting nutrition knowledge you can boast about to your friends. Best-case scenario, you'll have your six pack, feel more confident than you could have thought possible, and look damn good in that bikini. Win/win/win!

SO, ARE YOU READY TO GET STARTED? GOOD. LET'S DO IT!

Part One:
KNOWLEDGE IS POWER

CHAPTER ONE

WHY DIETING DOESN'T WORK

Most people see diets as temporary. And you know what? That's exactly what they are... temporary, not long-term. They're something you do for a certain period of time, and when you're done, you're back to your old habits. That's if you even finish the diet "plan," let alone continue what you've learned after it's over.

I get it, diets are ridiculous! They set ridiculous restrictions and even more ridiculous expectations. If you don't follow them to a T or don't notice any results after three days, you say, "F**k this; I'm over it!" and resort back to your pre-diet eating habits. It feels like diets are easy to start, even easier to quit, and set you up for failure before you even begin. Why? Because they are, at heart, temporary! They are not meant to be something you keep up for the rest of your life.

So why do we continue to buy into these diets if they don't work? Well, because we're human. We like to believe something we read and (try to) follow can help us get to where we want to be. There's nothing wrong with thinking this way. The way I see it, it's this very mode of thought that's preventing us from getting results that last a lifetime, not a month. To get there, habits need to be rebuilt, molded, and hardened. It takes months, even years, to truly change a habit. To get there, I'm not going to ask you to make changes based solely on your diet. I'm going to ask you to make changes based on your lifestyle.

So, why dump the word "diet," and replace it with "lifestyle?" There's two main reasons:

REALISTIC: You know yourself. You know that the ever-present seduction of an entire late-night pizza can beckon from time to time. You also know diets treat this yearning with fear and horror, and demand that you suppress it. Well, when you finish the diet "plan" and go back to giving in, do you really think the calories that come with it don't? Making changes to your lifestyle, on the other hand, comes with the knowledge that food is only one chapter in the book of health.

SUSTAINABLE: The way I see it, approaching what you put into your body isn't a question of what, but how and why. If you equip yourself with the right tools to understand why some nutrients are better (or worse) than others, the right skills to begin to build new lifestyle habits will follow. In short, "diets" always have some end date involved. Lifestyle changes do not.

You understand that you need to get back on track and you know that you can. You know that being there is awesome, but getting there sucks. Well, with the run-down on nutrients, recipes, and other healthy tips and suggestions that follow, I think that you too will have all the tools you need to make those little tweaks in your life that will help you finally stop settling for less. Now let's figure out how to get there.

page 128

page 80

CHAPTER TWO

YOUR SECRET WEAPON = MACRONUTRIENTS

You've probably seen the word "macros," otherwise known as "macronutrients," pop up a dozen times while scrolling through your Instagram feed (well, that's if you follow any fitness fanatics like me). Why though? They're hands-down the most important thing you need to understand about nutrition if you want to get rid of your stubborn belly fat and actually have enough energy to enjoy it. So yeah, they're a pretty big deal.

Macros are energy sources we get from eating food. These energy sources are fats, carbohydrates (carbs), and protein. Together they create calories (energy). They're essential to our survival. This is why elimination diets don't work. You remove one of these macros, and bad things are bound to happen. Your body will be thrown out of whack. Fat will begin to be stored in places it's never been before. Energy levels will begin to plummet faster than you can say "coffee, please." And your body will begin to eat itself, literally. Doesn't really sound like a great time. Well, that's what happens when you decide to mess with your body's energy sources. *Don't do it.*

So how do these macros relate to calories? Each gram of fat, protein, and carbs produce a certain amount of calories (energy) for the body to use. This is the exact breakdown:

Fats: 9 calories/gram

Carbs: 4 calories/gram

Proteins: 4 calories/gram

If you have a surplus of unused energy, it will turn into fat. If you have a deficit of energy, you will burn fat. In other words, if you eat too much and don't burn it off (you don't get off your butt), you will gain weight. If you eat the right amount and work off more than you eat (you get off your butt), you will burn fat. Now, there is a right, and a wrong way to do this. I *do not* recommend starving yourself and then working out like a fitness maniac to shed some pounds. That's extremely dangerous, and the perfect recipe for an overnight visit to the hospital. However, I *do* recommend finding a healthy balance of macros and pairing it with a fitness regimen that's customized to reaching your goals, whether that's to lose stubborn belly fat, or to build up that butt.

Let's look at a classic diet scenario. You've tried to follow your two or three friends' diet plans with them, and probably received two wildly inconsistent results. Well, take a look around you. Does everyone have exactly the same body, metabolism, and lifestyle? No. So why would generic advice work for everyone? It doesn't. What works is following a plan that's based off your body and needs. Someone who is 6'5" and 220 lbs is going to burn through what he/she eats differently than someone who is 5'4" and 110 lbs. It's science, and I have the facts to back it up.

Macro counting centers around you, not others. Your gender, age, weight, height, daily activity level and fitness goals (gain muscle or lose weight) all play a role in how many grams of calories, fats, carbs, and protein you need to eat per day to get the body of your dreams. By the way, are you starting to see why I was telling you to drop "diets" from the start? They're cookie-cutter. You're not, nor are your goals.

Hold up though. Before we even start getting into the nitty gritty of macros, I want to remind you of something: Don't skip any sections of this book! That means resisting the urge to go straight to calculating things. You made a promise at the beginning of this book, so don't do me dirty now. Stick to the plan and follow along. Remember, knowledge is power, so keep learning.

CHAPTER THREE:

THE NO BS TRUTH ABOUT FATS

Contrary to popular belief, fat is NOT the enemy; in fact, we need it to survive. Why? Think of it as fuel; it's what our body burns to keep our engines humming. Fat helps absorb vital vitamins and minerals, and is essential for blood clotting, muscle moving, and inflammation. However, not all fats are created equal. Good fats include monounsaturated and polyunsaturated fats. Bad ones include **trans fats**. **Saturated fats** fall somewhere in the middle. (I know, they're big words. But they're nice to know, and help you build those lifestyle changes I keep harping about.)

So, here's the differences between all these fats. Stick with me...

THE GOOD FATS:

When looking at a nutrition label, you're going to find some long words in relation to fat. Zoom in on if you can find "unsaturated" or not. Unsaturated fats, whether monounsaturated or polyunsaturated, are good fats your body wants to use.

Unsaturated fats are the king of fats, and provide a ton of benefits, including reducing your risk of cancer, stroke, and heart disease — pretty damn important stuff. They also strengthen your bones and can even improve your mood. (Down in the dumps? Grab some olive oil and call it a day.)

Well, guess what: These healthy monounsaturated and polyunsaturated fats will actually help you lose weight! The American Journal of Clinical Nutrition published a study in April 2009[1] that found that unsaturated fats keep you full and satisfied longer, which helps prevent overeating. *Eat less calories; lose more weight. That's how it works.*

Some of my favorite foods that are high in unsaturated fats include:

Olive oil

Canola oil

Sesame oil

Olives

Peanut butter

Almonds

Cashews

Walnuts

Avocado

Tofu

Sunflower seeds

Chia seeds

Wild-caught fish, including salmon, mackerel, and trout

[1] http://ajcn.nutrition.org/content/89/4/1019.abstract

Polyunsaturated fats have one important difference from monounsaturated fats: they provide omega-6 and omega-3 fatty acids. Your body needs these acids, but they happen to be the only two fatty acids your body can't naturally produce, which is why it's important to seek them out in your food choices. Fortunately, they can be found in some pretty tasty foods, including fish; chia, flax, and hemp seeds; and certain types of oils. Not a fan of these foods? If all else fails, take fish oil supplements, but make sure to get them into your body. They keep your heart in tip-top shape and are known to have anti-inflammatory effects.

To recap, unsaturated fats (polyunsaturated and monounsaturated) are good. Polyunsaturated fats contain omega-6 and omega-3 fatty acids; monounsaturated fats don't. Eat both. Got it? Good. Let's keep going.

THE BAD FATS:

The way I see it, **trans fats** are the worst type of fats that exist. Think deep-fried Oreos smothered in full-fat ice cream. That fair-food favorite is pretty much a heart attack on a plate. **Trans fats** are found in fatty meats and dairy, but are known for being in fried foods, cakes, and cookies. Not only will they give you a heart attack, literally, but they also contribute to high cholesterol, Type-2 diabetes, and stroke.

Fortunately, several countries, states, and cities have taken a stand against allowing this type of fat to enter anyone's body by restricting its use in food establishments. However, its use is not banned everywhere, so be conscious of this when ordering food out and when buying pre-packaged foods. In general, you can pretty much assume that anything at fast food chains on busy intersections contains trans fats. When shopping, check your nutrition labels. Even if it doesn't say **"trans fat"** under the fat section, if **"partially hydrogenated oils"** is listed in the ingredient list, it has **trans fat**.

To recap, trans fats, otherwise known as **partially hydrogenated oils**, are bad. It's a good idea to limit the amount of **trans fats** in your diet as much as possible. The less you eat, the better.

THE "OK" FATS:

You should generally limit your saturated fats as much as possible. They aren't as bad as **trans fats**, but they aren't considered to be "good." Saturated fat is the white swirly fat you see on pieces of meat. Gross, I know. Well, this same compound surrounds your waistline. Grosser, I know. Not to make you cringe (actually, yes to make you cringe), but saturated fat is a major contributor to your worst nightmare, cellulite. And that is all besides causing heart disease, high cholesterol, and stroke.

So, how do you dodge saturated fat? To start, you should limit these foods as much as possible:

Fatty beef and pork

Lamb

Chicken with skin

Lard and cream

Butter

Cheese (I know, I love cheese too, but would you rather have cellulite? Exactly.)

Other dairy products made from whole or 2% milk

Cookies, cakes, fries, and chips

THE AMERICAN HEART ASSOCIATION RECOMMENDS NO MORE THAN 5%–6% OF CALORIES IN YOUR DIET SHOULD BE FROM SATURATED FAT. FOR EXAMPLE, IF YOU EAT ABOUT 2000 CALORIES A DAY, NO MORE THAN 120 OF THEM SHOULD COME FROM SATURATED FATS. THAT'S ABOUT 13 GRAMS OF SATURATED FATS A DAY.

WHY ARE COCONUTS HEALTHY IF THEY'RE LOADED WITH SATURATED FAT?

Well, you've probably heard about the recent coconut craze. It's a funny sentence, but it's true: oil, flakes, conditioner, who knows what else. I personally think that coconuts provide a strong nutritional base, but I also think there's a lot of information out there about them that gets overlooked.

For example, yes, they primarily contain **saturated fat**, however, *they don't contain cholesterol*. Why? Coconuts are composed predominantly of (long word warning) medium-chain fatty acids, or MCFAs. Long story short, these medium-chain fatty acids are good for you. MCFAs raise good cholesterol levels and have also been shown to fight viruses and bacteria. This is a rare combo, and a core reason why the coconut craze is, well, a craze. So don't hold back when you get to the chocolate coconut mug cake on page 174. It's good for you.

To recap, limit the amount of **saturated fats** you eat as much as possible. If you like coconuts, eat coconuts. They are good for you and contain no cholesterol.

One last heads-up: At the end of the day, even though certain types are better than others, fat is still fat. Eat it in moderation, and remember that **all fats (good and bad) contain 9 calories per gram**, over twice the ratio of carbs and proteins. Keep this in mind when planning your meals.

page 174

CHAPTER FOUR

THE NO BS TRUTH ABOUT PROTEIN

The way I see it, it doesn't matter if you're trying to lose fat or gain muscle: protein is key. Let's start off addressing a common misconception about protein: First off, it will NOT make you look like a bodybuilder on steroids (unless, of course, that's what you're going for). In fact, eating the right amount of protein is just as important as a solid exercise plan when trying to look and feel damn good. By that I mean toned, strong, and fit. I think those are pretty good reasons to be obsessed.

So how does protein work? I'm not a doctor, but I can tell you that protein is made of amino acids, a chemical compound the human body needs to keep working like a well-oiled machine. The human body needs 22 of them to function, but it can only produce 13 of them itself. You get the other nine from food.

They're called essential amino acids.

This is when your food choices come into play. In general, animal-based proteins like meat, dairy, and eggs each contain these nine essential amino acids. That is to say, a tasty chicken breast, or skinny Greek omelet (recipe on page 90), will provide all nine.

Don't eat meat? No problem.

This is where I note another important pillar of knowledge: You find all nine of those essential amino acids in *animal-based* protein sources, but **not** all *plant-based* protein sources. This means certain grains, nuts, beans, and some soy products can be rich in a few of those amino acids, but sorely lacking in others. These foods are called "incomplete" protein sources. If you don't eat animal

products, this makes getting all 9 essential amino acids a little tricky, but not impossible.

The way I see it, when planning meat-free meals, pairing two of these "incomplete" protein sources is the best way to get all 9 essential amino acids. For example, beans and brown rice create a complete protein when paired together. Same with pairing peanut butter and whole-grain bread. Yes, that means those PB&J sandwiches can stay.

A good rule of thumb when pairing incomplete proteins is to combine grains, such as whole grain bread or rice, with legumes (beans, lentils, and nuts, to name a few), and voilà, you've got yourself a meal covering all the protein bases! So if you're not a fan of eating meat five times a day, plant proteins work just as well if paired the right way.

THE TRUTH ABOUT PROTEIN POWDER

Wait, what? That "stuff" those musclebound, grunting dudes in the weight area next to the ellipticals fill themselves with? Yes. That "stuff" is called protein powder. There's a certain gender (women) that tends to think protein powder is only for testosterone-pumping men. Nope.

The way I see it, because women tend to avoid the meat binges that men concuss themselves with, women need protein powder more than men. Yes, you too (assuming you're a woman. If you're a guy, this is still useful stuff to know.) Women are more likely than men to nibble on granola, cheese, and pretzel

page 84

thins with hummus. As a woman, I can confidently state that meat is less of a staple in our eating habits than men, and that many of the girls I talk to about protein powder give me the "You're joking, right?" look. I used to have this bias against protein powder myself. Then one day I decided to educate myself on the subject instead of believing all the hype, and realized I was an idiot for knocking protein powder for years.

Protein powder, like protein in general, will not make you look like the Hulk on steroids, unless you drink five protein shakes a day and spend your entire existence on the squat rack. However, I'm not recommending you do either of these things if your goal is to live a healthy and thriving lifestyle.

HOW TO PICK THE BEST PROTEIN POWDER FOR YOU

The most common type of protein powder is whey protein, which is made from cow's milk. Dairy-free and animal-free protein alternatives include vegan and vegetarian protein powders, which are made from plants. There's no universal right, or wrong, protein powder out there. Just like your macro count,

protein powder differs based on your body profile and preferences. In general, when picking out a protein powder, it's a good idea to follow these guidelines:

1. Look for powders without a list of ingredients you can't pronounce (AKA preservatives). Whey protein powders tend to have more of this junk, so as I keep repeating like a broken record, read your nutrition labels.

2. Look for powders that contain 20–25 grams of protein per scoop. This is plenty per serving to maintain a healthy lifestyle.

3. Gotta go whey? Look for ones labeled "isolate." Compared to other types of whey, isolate powders typically contain more protein per gram, and less fat, carbs, and lactose.

4. Avoiding whey? If you're searching for a plant-based powder, look for brands that contain a blend of rice, pea, and quinoa proteins in order to get all 9 of those essential amino acids.

So, now the question is: how much protein powder is enough? On average, one scoop of protein powder is equal to 20–25 grams of protein. A typical protein

shake contains 1 scoop of protein powder (20–25 grams of protein). One shake is typically more than enough to consume on a daily basis. This is because on average, each of your meals should contain around 20–25 grams of protein. *Has 20–25 grams been engrained in your head yet?* As mentioned before, the goal is to get the majority of your protein intake from food. However, as we know, women generally struggle to eat enough protein, which is why I believe protein powder can change the game for us ladies.

Now that we've addressed the elephant in the room, I encourage you to embrace protein powder as a supplement used in moderation for food-based protein moving forward. Not sure what brands are best? Keep a lookout for the brands I recommend on page 60.

HOW PROTEIN HELPS YOU LOSE WEIGHT AND BUILD MUSCLE

Ok, it's time to get into the real interesting stuff. Protein's main job is to build and maintain muscle tissue. The more you work out, the more protein you will need to eat. When you exercise, you create tiny tears in your muscles. In order to repair those tears and become stronger, you need to feed your muscles with protein. The 9 essential amino acids found in protein feed and repair your muscles. If you don't get all 9, or enough protein in general, you won't recover as well, and your muscles won't get the food they need to keep growing. So regardless of how much you work out, if you don't eat enough protein, you will not get the results you want. Experiencing weakness, pain, or flabbiness where there once used to be muscle is another side effect of not eating enough protein. When you don't eat enough protein, your muscles start to break down to supplement calories (food) instead of using the protein you eat to build muscles, tissues, and cells. So yeah, eat your protein.

Beyond that, the more muscle you generally have, the more fat (and therefore calories) you will generally burn. When you constantly burn fat, your body is constantly burning calories. In other words, your metabolism is kicking ass. The benefit of this is you can eat more, and still be fit.

No, this is not a typo.

As crazy as it sounds, the more muscle you gain, the more you can eat, and who doesn't love to eat? Just keep in mind that more food doesn't mean more unhealthy food; an XL pizza after three straight gym days is a great way to get right back to where you started. It's ok to indulge every once in awhile. Hell, live a little! But if eating like crap becomes a habit, you'll lose your results faster than you got them.

WHEN TO EAT PROTEIN

When you eat protein is just as important as how much you eat. A good rule of thumb is to intake protein *within 30 minutes* of finishing your workout, as that's the time when stressed and tired muscles are desperate for more fuel. Beyond that though, it's important to consider how to distribute your protein intake throughout the day. Let's look at a hypothetical eating schedule paired with typical protein amounts:

The typical small breakfast contains pretty much zero protein. I'm talking about a tiny flavored yogurt or a bowl of sugary processed cereal. Let's clock breakfast at around 8 grams of protein.

Snacks usually consist of a processed granola bar or one piece of fruit. *Satisfying.* Let's clock snacks at around 5 grams of protein.

Lunch is usually a little better. A turkey sandwich smothered in full-fat mayo and cheese, and oh, maybe some lettuce. Add a side of processed chips; can't forget that. Let's clock lunch at around 20 grams of protein.

Dinner is the big finale, serving up a huge slab of meat with some processed carb (flour tortillas), and maybe a side of veggies (again, lettuce). Let's clock dinner at around 30 grams of protein. That's a hypothetical day's worth of protein, clocking in at around 63 grams, and that's being generous.

If this sounds like your daily eating routine, well, where do I even start? First, that word "processed" was in almost everything listed above. We talked about this, and the processed junk needs to go. Second, let's point out the general lack of nutrition. I mean, lettuce, really? At least upgrade to spinach. Third, let's point out the carbs at EVERY meal. Unless you're Michael Phelps or run marathons for a living, cut down the carbs.

Fourth, let's point out that 63 grams of protein is plenty for a daily average… if you're a child. (Don't worry, we'll get to calculating how much you should eat soon.) And lastly, let's point out that the largest meal is dinner. If food provides you with energy, wouldn't it make sense to eat your largest meal in the morning, not before knocking out for 6–10 hours? Hmm… I think we are starting to get somewhere…

Ok, back to why spreading out your protein is important. Your body can only absorb and use a certain amount of protein at one time, and whatever is left becomes waste. So the way I see it, it's better to spread your protein over 3–5 meals, rather than mixing low-protein meals with massive ones. In general, it's better to eat higher amounts of protein in the morning and directly after you exercise. As I said above, your body craves protein at these times. Listen to it.

CHAPTER FIVE:

THE NO BS TRUTH ABOUT CARBS

There's a lot of bad talk about carbs making America "fat." Yet, carbs are huge sources of energy, and are essential in any healthy and balanced diet. They're also in almost everything we eat. Carbs are the sugars, starches, and fibers found in fruits, grains, vegetables, beans, dairy products, and so on. So that whole "let's cut all carbs" diet really means something more like, "let's just deprive ourselves of very important nutrients."

So why do carbs get a bad rep? The way I see it, much of it's because people don't understand what a carbohydrate really is. There are actually two types: simple carbs and complex carbs. **Simple is bad,** complex is good. *Simple, right?*

WHAT ARE SIMPLE CARBS, AKA "BAD CARBS"?

Simple carbs, simply put, are sugar. Sugar turns into fat. The more sugar you eat, the more fat you gain. As straightforward as it sounds, a lot of people don't get that *no matter what kind of sugar you eat, your body turns it into fat*. You bought this book because you want to have a healthier lifestyle, right? Here's another hard truth then: cut down on your sugar intake. **A LOT.**

Simple carbs are found in processed foods including candies, syrups, cakes, cookies, donuts, fruit juices, cereals, white bread, white rice, and sodas. In other words, processed junk. These processed foods give you an energy (sugar) high, followed by an energy low. For example, when you first eat a candy bar, you feel like you're walking on cloud nine. Then about an hour later, you feel like your cloud crashed into a brick wall. You know the feeling. It's why two pieces of chocolate cake for lunch could have you near-asleep at your desk by quitting time. Your body is greedy and processes all that sugar like it's going out of style. Then before you know it, you're hungry, irritable, and don't want to get off of the couch. See why I said to cut down on the sugar?

But wait, not ALL simple carbs are bad...

Fruits and some veggies contain simple carbs. Fruit is full of *natural (AKA unprocessed)* sugars, and simple carbs are pretty much sugar.

You know that fruit is healthy. The reason why you can handle the sugars that come from fruit is because they're loaded with essential vitamins and nutrients, like fiber and vitamin C. As a result, fruit is processed more like complex carbs, AKA the "good carbs." Keep in mind, though, that sugar is sugar, and fruit has a lot of it. Unless you're a bodybuilder or have diabetes, fruit is not something you need to eliminate from your diet. Just don't go crazy and eat three bananas, two apples, and an orange in the same day. *Limit your fruit intake to 2–3 servings/day and opt for fruits that are naturally lower in sugar, but rich in vitamins and nutrients, like berries.*

page 100

page 146

page 74

WHAT ARE COMPLEX CARBS, AKA "GOOD CARBS"?

Complex carbs are your new best friend. They're loaded with fiber and other essential nutrients that provide your body with real, sustained energy, not that sugary crap. Not to mention, all that fiber controls your appetite, so you won't mindlessly snack on those chocolate chip cookies hiding in your desk drawer.

Below is a list of some of my favorite *gluten-free* complex carbs:

Acorn Squash

Black Beans

Black-Eyed Peas

Buckwheat

Butternut Squash

Corn

Garbanzo Beans (chickpeas)

Green Peas

Kidney Beans

Lentils

Lima Beans

Navy Beans

Oatmeal

Oats

Parsnips

Pinto Beans

Quinoa

Rice (brown, colored, and wild)

Split Peas

Sweet Potato

Don't care about eating gluten-free? Add wheat, rye, and barley to this list.

To recap, cookies are bad; brown rice is good. Cookies will give you temporary crappy energy; brown rice will give you awesomely sustained energy. Cookies will leave you wanting to eat more; brown rice will keep you full and satisfied (generally speaking). The way I see it, it's very important to choose unprocessed complex carbs as much as possible, and limit processed sugar-loaded simple carbs as much as possible. You will feel better, and your waistline will too.

CHAPTER SIX:

WHY FIBER IS THE SH*T

Fiber is awesome. It helps you poop.

Now before you get grossed out (if this hasn't happened already), let's talk about why. Fiber helps clean up your digestive system to help it run smoothly; more poetically put, it literally helps get the "crap" out of our of bodies, which is why it's such an important nutrient. Fiber also helps you stay full, and even helps control cholesterol levels. Win/win!

If you're lacking fiber in your diet, AKA you're constipated— let's call it what it is— run to the store and buy these foods ASAP:

Fruits

Vegetables

Nuts

Beans

Whole grains

On average, it's recommended that women consume 25 grams of fiber per day, and that men consume 38 grams of fiber per day. Getting as close to these averages as possible will ensure you get an ample amount of fiber in your diet.

A HIGH-FIBER FOOD CONTAINS AT LEAST FIVE GRAMS OF FIBER PER SERVING. A GOOD-FIBER FOOD CONTAINS BETWEEN 2.5 AND 4.9 GRAMS PER SERVING.

page 178

When on vacation, these rules don't apply. OK, still keep them in the back of your head. But when a local chef offers you a homemade treat in Bali, it would be rude not graciously accept.

CHAPTER SEVEN:

WHY SUGAR IS THE REAL ENEMY

You've learned that sugar turns into fat, and excess fat equals love handles and cellulite. But if sugar is so bad, why can't we stop eating it? Sugar is addictive, so much so that scientists have found it stimulates the same pleasure centers of the brain as cocaine or heroin[2]. Talk about a gateway drug.

I bring this up because monitoring your sugar intake is just as important as the amount of carbs, fats, and proteins you're eating. You know that sugar is in cakes, candy, and soda, but it has also snuck its way into almost everything else you buy, even the foods that you consider to be "healthy." Foods labeled "all-natural" or "organic" are typically loaded with added sugar. For example, ketchup, dressings, oatmeal packets, flavored nuts, and organic granola all sound healthy, but they almost always contain added sugar. That's why I've mentioned at least a dozen times to read the damn nutrition label! Seriously. When reading a nutrition label, if sugar is one of the first few ingredients listed, or if it contains more than 15 grams of sugar per serving, it's not your best option. This includes your favorite "organic" granola bar that packs in a whopping 25 grams of sugar. I don't care if the sugar is "natural;" put the bar down. That goes for anything made with excess amounts of honey, maple syrup, and agave nectar. Sorry to be the bearer of bad news, but these "natural" sweeteners are pure sugar. The less you eat, the better, trust me.

[2] http://journals.plos.org/plosone/article?id=10.1371/journal.pone.0000698

CHAPTER EIGHT

BOOZE EXPLAINED, SIP-BY-SIP

Since this book is based on being realistic, we need to realistically talk about how to handle drinking alcohol. I'm referring to beer, wine, liquor, and everything "alcohol-related" in between. If you don't drink alcohol, great! You have one less thing to worry about. However, if you enjoy a glass of red wine or an ice cold beer after a long day at work, we need to get really honest about what and how much you're really drinking.

THE TRUTH ABOUT WHAT YOU'RE DRINKING

So you like to drink, but do you really know what you're drinking? Alcohol is sugar, and you already know what sugar leads to... excess fat. Mind-Blowing Alcohol Fact No. 1: Gram for gram, alcohol is nearly twice as calorie-dense as sugar, which makes a vodka cranberry even more dangerous than a big slice of chocolate cake.

It seems ridiculous to compare drinking a Blue Moon to eating a Snickers, but the reality is it's not much different. Have you noticed the lack of calorie counts on your favorite alcoholic beverage? Maybe yes, maybe no, maybe you don't care to look. Mind-Blowing Alcohol Fact No. 2: The truth is nutrition

labels are not required for alcohol products, which makes it even easier (as if it wasn't already easy enough) to drink, drink, and drink, and not think twice about it.

With this in mind, think about how many alcoholic beverages you drink a week. One? Five? Ten? Maybe more? Even one drink a day can quickly add up.

To get an idea of just how quickly, let's look at a hypothetical drinking scenario: On average, a 5 oz. glass of red wine contains 125 calories (Note, 5 oz., not the whole damn bottle). If you drink four, 5 oz. glasses of wine on your big night out (which is probably more like five or six glasses according to bartender standards), that equals at least 500 calories. These 500 calories are in addition to the calories you ate earlier to survive. Let's not forget about the late-night pizza you happily scarfed down on your way home. So between the wine, pizza, and the food you ate to function, a sh*t-ton of calories were consumed. Told you it adds up quick.

HOW TO HAVE YOUR DRINK AND CAKE TOO

There's nothing wrong with the occasional drink. However, calories add up when you blindly drink in excess. Maybe you know how many calories are in your favorite craft beer, but most likely not. Knowledge is power, and power gives you control. Regain that control by knowing what you're drinking. Since alcoholic drinks don't contain nutrition information, use this list as a calorie reference:

5 oz. glass of champagne- 84 calories

5 oz. glass of red wine- 125 calories

5 oz. glass of white wine- 121 calories

12 oz. regular beer- 153 calories

12 oz. light beer- 103 calories

2.25 oz. Martini- 124 calories

2.75 oz. Cosmo-146 calories

4 oz. Margarita-168 calories

3.5 oz. Manhattan- 164 calories

9 oz. Piña Colada- 490 calories

1.5 oz. shot of 80 proof liquor (gin, rum, soda, whiskey, tequila)- 97 calories

*Calorie amounts are averages, and are not based off specific brands.

Still don't know what drinks are best? Here are some facts that will help you make good choices when ordering drinks:

- Tonic water is loaded with sugar. Seltzer water and club soda have no sugar and zero calories.

- Fancy cocktails with two or more mixtures have more calories and sugar than cocktails with a ratio of 1 liquor : 1 mixer. Opt for the vodka club soda before the Sex on the Beach.

- Avoid juice and sugary mixtures as much as possible to cut down on calories. Opt for fresh fruit to sweeten drinks as a lower calorie option.

- Craft beers are almost double in calories than regular beers. So drink one, not five.

- Red wine has more health benefits and typically less sugar than white wine.

- Sweet wines, such as moscato, prosecco, sherry, white zinfandel, rose, and riesling, have more calories than dry wines, such as pinot noir, cabernet, chardonnay, merlot, sauvignon blanc, champagne, and shiraz.

- One shot of 80 proof liquor has *97 calories*! That's a lot. I thought this fact needed to be restated.

To sum up booze, the less you drink, the better. When you drink, pay attention to how much you're drinking and what you're drinking to avoid unexpected massive amounts of calories. The simpler the drink, the smaller the calories. Cheers to that.

My recommendation: Skip the booze and sip on a fresh coconut. They taste amazing, are loaded with potassium, and instantly make you look like an A-list celeb.

Part Two:
USING YOUR KNOWLEDGE TO THRIVE

CHAPTER NINE

CALCULATING YOUR MACROS

I hate math, and if you're like me, you do too. I could try to explain how to calculate your macros by hand, but that would get messy, and you would say "f**k this!" after 10 minutes. Fortunately, my custom macro calculator does the math for you. Go to www.katiesampayo.com/macro-calculator, answer a few questions HONESTLY, and within seconds get your daily macronutrient results in your email inbox. Yes, it's that easy!

HOW TO USE MY CUSTOM MACRO CALCULATOR

Let's walk through, step by step, how to calculate your macros using my custom macro calculator. To show you how, we're going to calculate the macros for a woman with the following profile:

Age: 25
Weight: 125
Height: 5'4"
Occupation: Works a desk job from 9:00 am to 5:00 pm, 5 days a week
Exercise Frequency/Duration/Intensity: 3 days a week for 45 minutes at a moderate to high intensity, working up a sweat
Fitness Goal: Lose 10 pounds of fat over the next 2 months

STEP 1: CALCULATE YOUR TOTAL DAILY ENERGY EXPENDITURE (TDEE).

Total Daily Energy Expenditure (TDEE) is the amount of calories you burn per day. This includes calories you burn while sleeping, working, exercising, and pretty much any activity that uses energy. This number is crucial to know if you want to lose weight, gain weight, or maintain weight.

A: To calculate your TDEE, first enter your gender, age, height, and weight.

Step 1: Calculate Your Total Daily Energy Expenditure (TDEE)

TDEE is how many calories you burn per day when exercise is taken into account.

GENDER
○ Male
● Female

AGE
[25] years

HEIGHT
[5] Ft [4] In
● Imperial
○ Metric

WEIGHT
[125] lbs

B: Then, select your daily activity level, which includes your weekly amount of exercise and intensity of exercise. When selecting a category, really think about how active you are at your job and how many days on average you exercise each week. Then really think about how intensely you exercise, on a scale from easy to extremely intense. For example, a gentle flow yoga class, walking, or hopping on the elliptical for a few minutes without breaking a sweat does not count as moderate to difficult exercise. However, a barre class, vinyasa flow yoga class, or cardio interval training (running/jogging up and down hills) where you're working up a sweat and challenging yourself would be considered as moderate to difficult exercise.

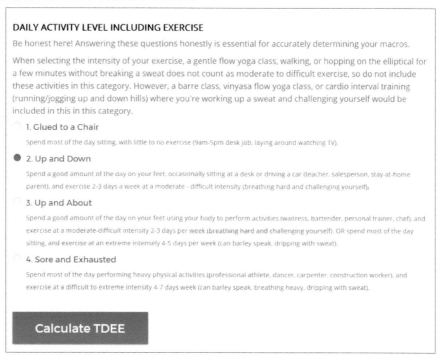

DAILY ACTIVITY LEVEL INCLUDING EXERCISE

Be honest here! Answering these questions honestly is essential for accurately determining your macros.

When selecting the intensity of your exercise, a gentle flow yoga class, walking, or hopping on the elliptical for a few minutes without breaking a sweat does not count as moderate to difficult exercise, so do not include these activities in this category. However, a barre class, vinyasa flow yoga class, or cardio interval training (running/jogging up and down hills) where you're working up a sweat and challenging yourself would be included in this in this category.

○ **1. Glued to a Chair**
Spend most of the day sitting, with little to no exercise (9am-5pm desk job, laying around watching TV).

● **2. Up and Down**
Spend a good amount of the day on your feet, occasionally sitting at a desk or driving a car (teacher, salesperson, stay-at-home parent), and exercise 2-3 days a week at a moderate - difficult intensity (breathing hard and challenging yourself).

○ **3. Up and About**
Spend a good amount of the day on your feet using your body to perform activities (waitress, bartender, personal trainer, chef), and exercise at a moderate-difficult intensity 2-3 days per week (breathing hard and challenging yourself), OR spend most of the day sitting, and exercise at an extreme intensely 4-5 days per week (can barley speak, dripping with sweat).

○ **4. Sore and Exhausted**
Spend most of the day performing heavy physical activities (professional athlete, dancer, carpenter, construction worker), and exercise at a difficult to extreme intensity 4-7 days week (can barley speak, breathing heavy, dripping with sweat).

Calculate TDEE

Based on the woman in our example who works a desk job and exercises 3 days a week for 45 minutes at a moderate to high intensity, she selects the Up and Down category. However, if she exercised 1–2 days a week at a moderate intensity, she would select the Glued to a Chair category.

STEP 2: SELECT YOUR GOALS AND INTENSITY.

Once you calculate your TDEE, select your fitness goals—whether they're to lose weight/body fat, maintain what you have, or gain muscle mass/weight.

For example, because the woman in our example wants to lose 10 pounds of fat over the next 2 months, she selects Moderate Fat Loss (15%). However, if she wanted to lose 10 pounds in 1 month, she would select Aggressive Fat Loss (20%). If you like your body as it is now and want to maintain what you have, select Maintain What You Have (Same as TDEE).

If you're happy with your body fat and want to focus on building muscle and becoming more toned (getting that butt), select Moderate Muscle Gain (15%). If you're focused strictly on gaining muscle-mass (competing in a bodybuilding/bikini competition, are an athlete, or are ready to take your muscle-mass to another level) select Aggressive Muscle Gain (20%).

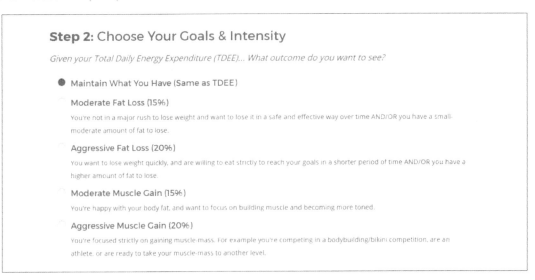

STEP 3: CUSTOMIZE YOUR NUTRITION PLAN.

Next, customize your nutrition plan by specifying how much protein and fat you need to consume to reach your goals. Carbs are automatically calculated after calories from protein and fat have been subtracted from your TDEE.

Remember what we learned about how calories relate to protein, fat, and carbs? If not, refer to Chapter 2 or the chart below for a quick recap:

Proteins: 4 calories/gram
Fats: 9 calories/gram
Carbs: 4 calories/gram

With this information in mind, in the calculator I preselected .8 g/lb of body weight of protein and .35 g/lb of body weight of fat. I recommend leaving these selections as is, unless a personal trainer or nutritionist has provided you with specific amounts of protein and/or fat to consume based on your goals (lose weight, gain muscle, or maintain).

However, if you really want to get specific but don't have access to a personal trainer or nutritionist, below is a summary of how to select other protein and fat amounts.

Protein: If you want to gain muscle mass and are exercising at a difficult intensity more than 4 days a week, select .9 g/lb of body weight of protein. If you're a bodybuilder or an athlete, you can select as high as 1 g/lb of body weight of protein, but on average most people will fall into the .8 –.9 g/lb of body weight category when selecting protein intake.

Fat: If you're exercising intensely, you can select a higher amount of fat. Because fat is calorie-dense (9 calories/gram), if you're exercising intensely it will be used as a primary energy source. However, if you're not exercising intensely, keep .35 g/lb of body weight of fat selected.

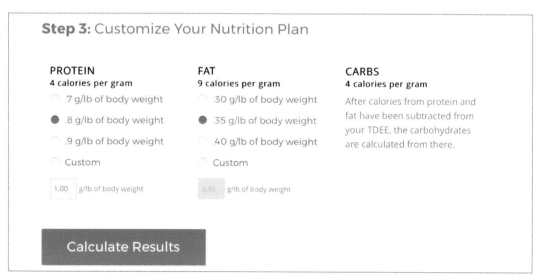

FINAL STEP: GET YOUR RESULTS!

Based on your answers from the previous steps, your macros are calculated. To put this together, the daily macros for the woman in our example are shown below:

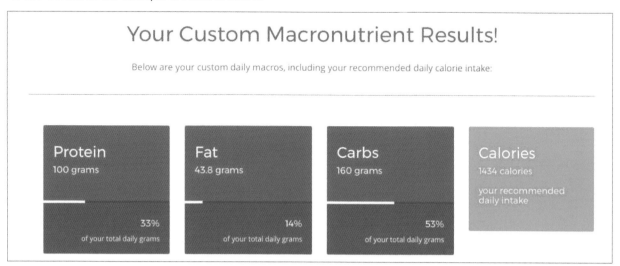

Your macros will be different because you are different. This is just an example to show you how the macro calculation process works.

I recommend updating your macros as your weight, age, activity level, and goals change. In general, it's good to rerun this calculation every month to make sure you're on track with reaching your goals.

HOW TO PUT EVERYTHING TOGETHER

After calculating your macros, you need to understand how to use them when planning your meals. In order to do this, let's recap what you've learned:

- Lifestyle changes work. Diets don't.

- Unsaturated fats promote heart health. Saturated and trans fats promote heart attacks.

- Complex carbs give you energy. Simple carbs make you crash.

- Fiber makes you poop. A lack of fiber makes you constipated.

- Protein makes you strong and lean. Chips and pizza make you fat and lazy.

- Muscle burns fat. Fat stores fat.

- Nutrients are good. Sugar is bad.

- Getting off your butt is good. Sitting on the couch is bad.

- Natural foods are healthy. Processed foods are unhealthy.

- Eating is heaven. Starving is hell.

- Following a plan equals success. Winging it equals mixed results.

- Coconuts are your friend. Fries are not.

- One drink is ok. Eight drinks are not.

Ok, so now you should have an idea of what works, and what doesn't, when it comes to living a healthy lifestyle. Now, apply these pillars of knowledge when planning your meals. For example, if your macros are 250 grams of carbs, 60 grams of fat, and 90 grams of protein, opt for the salmon filet with asparagus and sweet potatoes, not the artery-clogging burger with fries.

Disclaimer: Following your macro counts is not a free pass to eating whatever you want. If you want to stop settling and start thriving, don't treat this like some half-assed attempt at a diet. You already know diets don't work because they're temporary, so stop thinking in temporary terms. Treat your body like the sacred temple it is, and reap the rewards. This book is based on living a healthy lifestyle, not sneaking temporary shortcuts that lead to temporary results. Yeah, sure, you could technically scarf down that juicy burger with fries to get your 250 grams of carbs, 60 grams of fat, and 90 grams of protein... But I don't need to remind you that it would be the opposite of living a healthy lifestyle. Use this knowledge wisely, and don't fool yourself.

TOOLS TO HELP YOU KEEP TRACK

Thanks to technology, keeping track of your macros is now easier than ever before.

MyFitnessPal is an app you can use on your smartphone or tablet to keep track of your macros so you don't have to spend hours calculating and logging them with pen and paper. When you first set up your account, enter your macronutrient goals calculated with my calculator (fats, carbs, proteins, and calories). You can enter them as a percent for free (see picture on right). You can also enter your macros into the app as grams. I prefer this method because it tracks your macros more accurately. However, this method is only available in the paid version of the app. If you don't care about being exactly on point with tracking your macros, opt for the free version. Otherwise, upgrade to the paid version for more accurate results.

MyFitnessPal tracks your progress toward reaching your daily macronutrient goals based on the foods you enter into the app. However, this only works if you enter these foods into the app. The app does not know what you're eating unless you tell it. If you don't, it will not calculate and track your macros, which defeats the purpose of

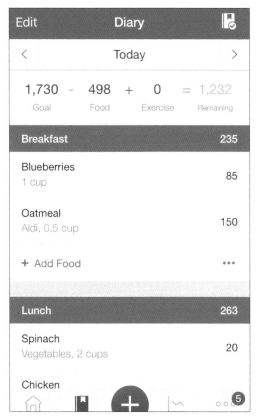

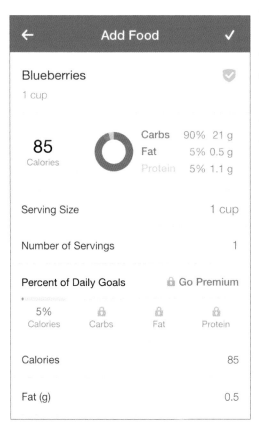

using the app. So, don't be lazy, and enter in EVERYTHING you eat. Even the handful of nuts you ate when rushing out the door. That's food, and food contains macros, so it needs to be calculated.

Thankfully, MyFitnessPal is preloaded with thousands of foods and restaurants, removing the process of manually calculating the amount of fat, protein, and carbs in everything you eat. For example, if you eat ½ cup of oatmeal with blueberries for breakfast, you simply type this into the search bar and the macros will be calculated and stored in seconds (see picture on left).

Otherwise, if manually calculating your macros is more your style, I suggest recording your daily macros in a journal dedicated to your new thriving lifestyle. Evaluate your progress at the end of the day, and use this information to make adjustments, if needed, for the next day.

COUNTING MACROS ISN'T FOREVER

When beginning this lifestyle change, it's extra important to consciously read nutrition labels and take notes on the macros you're consuming. After diligently doing this for a few weeks, things like when, what, and how much food to eat in order to maintain your healthy lifestyle will start becoming second nature. So, this whole intense tracking thing isn't forever, it's just to get you started until you begin to understand what foods contain what. Another surprise: You get better with practice. Before long, making smart food choices based off solid knowledge, instead of "whatever the diet of the month" is, will come naturally to you.

Remember: Knowledge is power, so keep learning after you finish reading this book. Know your body from the inside out, and know what foods, and what amounts, give you energy, make you feel great, and get you the body of your dreams.

CHAPTER TEN.

THE NO BS TRUTH ABOUT GLUTEN

Talk about a word that sounds like it could mean anything. Have you ever thought, "Um… this has gluten? What does gluten-free mean? What is Celiacs disease? Is this, "gluten-free diet", thing really all it's cracked up to be?"

I'm sure you've already noticed, but doesn't it seem like everyone from your mom's best friend to your next door neighbor is practicing this "gluten-free diet" thing? At first I didn't understand what all the hype was about. I mean, does your mom's best friend have Celiac disease, or is she blindly following this new "hot trend"? I needed to find out more. So, of course, I did my research.

ACCORDING TO THE CELIAC DISEASE FOUNDATION, "GLUTEN IS A GENERAL NAME FOR THE PROTEINS FOUND IN WHEAT (WHEATBERRIES, DURUM, EMMER, SEMOLINA, SPELT, FARINA, FARRO, GRAHAM, KAMUT® KHORASAN WHEAT AND EINKORN), RYE, BARLEY AND TRITICALE— A CROSS BETWEEN WHEAT AND RYE. GLUTEN HELPS FOODS MAINTAIN THEIR SHAPE, ACTING AS A GLUE THAT HOLDS FOOD TOGETHER."

So in a nutshell, gluten makes stuff stick together. It's found in wheat, rye, barley, and a grain called triticale; whatever that is. Cool, good to know. Now how does that affect us? Well, it really only affects a certain percentage of the population: those who are gluten-sensitive, gluten-intolerant, allergic to wheat, or have Celiac disease. So what's the difference between those who have a gluten sensitivity or allergy and those diagnosed with Celiac disease? People with

Celiac disease cannot physically absorb the nutrients from food when it passes through their small intestine, leading to malnutrition and even greater gastrointestinal problems. People who have a gluten sensitivity or a wheat allergy do not have these intense digestive issues, however, they can still experience discomfort or minor pain from consuming foods made with gluten. Just because you aren't lactose intolerant, doesn't mean the occasional yogurt can't give you a stomach ache. Simply put, if you *don't* have Celiac disease, your body can tolerate gluten (at the expense of personal discomfort). If you *have* Celiac disease your body cannot tolerate gluten at all.

The crazy thing is that 80 percent of people on gluten-free diets don't have Celiac disease. That's a lot of people cutting out wheat, but why? I wanted to find out for myself, so I decided to give this "gluten-free diet" thing a try. Now before you cast judgement, I want to reiterate that I hate diets, and stand behind what I said earlier about never partaking in one. I would call this an experiment, not a diet, that, believe it or not, turned into a lifestyle change.

After a bit of time cutting gluten from my diet, I realized that gluten does affect me. I noticed when I *didn't* eat gluten that I wouldn't feel bloated, and generally had more energy throughout the day. **My conclusion:** I don't have Celiac disease, but I am gluten-sensitive, and I now actively avoid eating gluten as much as possible.

The way I see it, just to make this clear: Not eating gluten isn't a diet; it's a lifestyle change, and for a lot of people, it's essential to their health.

So in case you haven't noticed, this book is entirely gluten-free. Surprise! Don't freak out. This doesn't change the core principles of this book. You're still throwing your diet-failing "ok" eating habits out the door and replacing them with a new and improved healthy lifestyle. You're going to love yourself and your life. You're going to thrive.

WHEN TO TOSS THE WHEAT

You don't need to throw out the wheat pasta and bring on the rice noodles to live a healthy lifestyle. However, in my experience as a trainer/nutrition expert, I've found that a lot of people suffer from gluten sensitivity without even knowing it.

Not sure if gluten is affecting you? Check out this list of common symptoms of gluten sensitivity:

Headache

Grogginess

Joint pain

Numbness in the legs, arms, and/or fingers

Diarrhea

Bloating

IBS (Irritable Bowel Syndrome)

If you experience any of these symptoms after eating gluten, consult your doctor for a proper diagnosis. Otherwise, you can assume that like the other 80 percent and I, (see reference on page 51) that gluten isn't your friend.

HOW TO EAT GLUTEN-FREE, WITHOUT BEING SCAMMED

In this book we do nothing half-assed. So, we won't be approaching gluten half-assed either. When eating gluten-free, the same principles apply as discussed earlier in this book: Processed? Nope. From the earth? Yep.

Before running to the store buying any and everything labeled "gluten-free," beware! From gluten-free cookies to gluten-free pizza, the whole thing is a giant money-making scam. Most of this stuff labeled "gluten-free" is processed junk (again a no-no) disguised in pretty healthy-looking packaging. Just another reason why you need to read nutrition labels and look for macros (fats, carbs, and proteins) when buying food. You will likely find high amounts of saturated fat (AKA cellulite), high amounts of sugar (AKA carbs), and a bunch of chemicals you can't pronounce (AKA preservatives).

When buying gluten-free, just like when buying any type of food, it's best to buy fresh and avoid processed food as much as possible. I believe it's also important not to be tricked into paying double for something because the label claims it's natural, healthy, and/or gluten-free. Don't be fooled. If you want to eat gluten-free, use the shopping list starting on page 60 and stick to it.

Part Three:
BEFORE YOU START COOKING

CHAPTER ELEVEN

INGREDIENT INFORMATION, KITCHEN ESSENTIALS, AND SHOPPING LISTS

You're excited to start cooking. It's taken you minutes, hours, days, or weeks to get to this point, and I know you want to eat already. The good thing is, we only have a little bit more to cover. I'm talking a few more minutes of reading; that's it. If you're thinking, "Yeah... I'm ready. Peace out, Chapter 11. I'm hungry and part 4 is calling my name!", **STOP** and remember the commitment you made at the beginning of this book.

Suddenly forget? Let me remind you. You agreed to read this entire book, and that includes Chapter 11. Besides, if you skip ahead to the recipes now, you will have no clue how to customize these recipes to best fit *your lifestyle and your macro counts.*

So bear with me. I promise this will be quick...

INGREDIENT INFORMATION

- Every ingredient is gluten-free.

- All eggs are large.

- Salt is either coarse sea salt or garlic salt; take your pick!

- Pepper is preferably freshly ground, black pepper.

- Olive oil is always extra-virgin olive oil (EVOO).

- Coconut oil is organic.

- Mayonnaise is organic.

- Dairy-free milk is used in every recipe. My favorite types are cashew milk, coconut milk, and almond milk.

- Peanut butter can be replaced with other nut butters, including almond butter, cashew butter, and sunflower seed butter.

- Peanut butter can be replaced with PB2 Powdered Peanut Butter (or any brand of peanut butter powder) to reduce fat and calories in a dish.

- Protein powder is measured at 20 grams of protein per scoop. Adjust your scoops based on the powder you use.

- Chia seeds, flax seeds, and hemp seeds can be used interchangeably.

- Flax seeds are milled or ground, not whole. Learn why on page 175.

- No processed sugar is used in this book. A list of natural sweeteners is included in your Shopping List on page 62.

- All natural sweeteners can be used interchangeably. **Note:** *Stevia will have the lowest impact on macro counts.*

- All bacon and sausage is nitrate-free. Learn why on page 88.

- Meat and seafood *do not need to be organic.* However, if you have room in your budget, splurge on these items:

  High-quality 100% grass-fed beef

  Uncured meats without nitrates/preservatives (sausage and bacon)

  Antibiotic-free chicken (hormone-free)

  Wild-caught fish

- Produce *does not need to be organic.* However, if you have room in your budget, buy the following items organic:

  Strawberries

  Apples

  Celery

  Grapes

  Spinach

  Tomatoes

  Bell peppers

  Cherry tomatoes

  Cucumbers

  Hot peppers

  Kale/Collard Greens

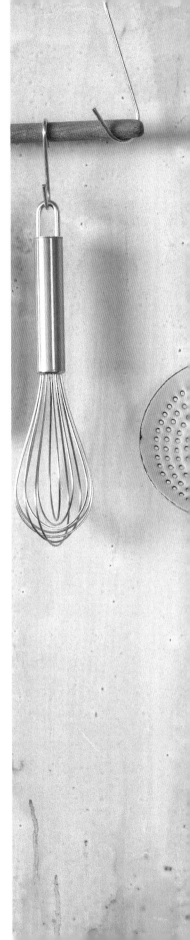

DIETARY SWAPS

- Grains can be swapped for cauliflower rice, or fresh greens, such as spinach or kale, if you need a lower carb option.

- Vegetables and grains are interchangeable. For example, quinoa can be swapped for brown rice, and spinach can be swapped for kale.

- All recipes can be made vegetarian/pescetarian-friendly by swapping any meat protein sources for tofu, tempeh, eggs or legumes, such as beans, nuts, lentils, and seafood (if you're pescetarian). Refer back to page 25 if you need help pairing plant proteins.

- All recipes can be made dairy-free by replacing dairy products with dairy-free substitutes, such as plant-based yogurt, plant-based protein powder, dairy-free milk, dairy-free cheese (or skip the cheese all-together), or organic mayo (naturally dairy-free).

KITCHEN ESSENTIALS

MUST HAVE
Food processor or high-powered blender
Measuring cups and spoons
Muffin tins
Baking sheets
Medium-size bowl
One good knife
Cutting board
Can opener
Storage containers
Aluminum foil

WOULD BE NICE
Grater
Meat thermometer
Food scale
Non-stick pots and pans
Mixing bowls
Garlic press
Lemon/lime juicer
Rubber spatula
Strainer
Parchment paper
Grill
Wok

SHOPPING LIST WITH MY MOST-LOVED BRANDS

Use these lists when shopping for foods used frequently in this book. Specific food items that I love are listed in parenthesis.

Keep in mind... This list *only* includes ingredients used frequently throughout this book. It's not an end-all-be-all guide to eating healthy. For example, broccoli and brussel sprouts are not included in this list. Both are super healthy, but they are not used in any recipes in this book, which is why they're not listed below. If you strictly use this list when shopping, you will eat extremely healthy. However, don't let it prevent you from buying your favorite fruit, veggie, or other healthy food if not listed below.

PROTEIN

Eggs
White albacore canned tuna in water
Nitrate-free uncured bacon
Nitrate-free natural turkey sausage (Butterball Natural Inspirations Turkey Sausage)
100% grass-fed lean ground beef
Pork chops
Lean ground turkey
Chicken breasts
Wild Alaskan sockeye salmon
Sushi-grade ahi tuna filets
White fish (cod, mahi mahi, tilapia)
Large, frozen, fully-cooked, and deveined shrimp
Tofu and/or tempeh
Protein powder (My favorite vegan powder is Orgain Organic Protein and my favorite whey isolate powder is Bodylogix Natural Whey).

HERBS & SPICES

Cumin
Chili powder
Red pepper flakes
Oregano
Cinnamon
Nutmeg
Sea salt
Garlic salt
Freshly ground black pepper
Bay leaves
Red curry paste
Ginger
Basil
Dill
Rosemary/thyme
Parsley
Cilantro

CONDIMENTS & SPREADS

Organic mayo (Primal Kitchen Avocado Oil Mayo)
Dijon mustard
Gluten-free, low-sodium soy sauce (San J Gluten-Free Tamari Lite Soy Sauce)
Hummus
Salsa
Natural creamy peanut butter and/or peanut butter powder (PB2 Peanut Butter Powder)
Bbq sauce (Trader Joes Carolina Gold BBQ Sauce)
Pesto
Chicken broth
Hoisin sauce (Lee Kum Kee Hoisin Sauce)

BAKING/DESSERT ESSENTIALS

Vanilla extract
Baking soda
Baking powder
Coconut flour or gluten-free flour blend (Bob's Red Mill Organic Coconut Flour)
Cocoa powder
Dark chocolate chips
Cacao nibs (Viva Naturals Organic Raw Cacao Nibs)
Coconut flakes (Edward & Sons 100% Organic Toasted Unsweetened Coconut Flakes)
Canned pumpkin puree

DAIRY/DAIRY SUBSTITUTES

Plain, nonfat Greek yogurt
Plant-based yogurt (So Delicious Coconut Milk Yogurt)
Fat-free or 1% milk-fat cottage cheese
Coconut milk
Unsweetened dairy-free milk (almond milk, cashew milk, coconut milk)
All-nautral whipped topping (So Delicious Light Coco Whip)
Fresh feta cheese, preferably soaked in brine
Freshly-grated parmesan cheese

OILS & VINEGARS

Extra Virgin Olive Oil (EVOO)
Organic coconut oil
EVOO cooking spray
Apple cider vinegar
Balsamic vinegar
White wine vinegar or dry white wine (Napa Valley Organic White Wine Vinegar)

NATURAL SWEETENERS

Natural honey
Agave nectar
Pure maple syrup
Stevia

BREADS/GRAINS

Gluten-free bread (Ezekiel Bread. Found in the freezer aisle of most grocery stores)
Quinoa
Brown rice
Whole-grain rolled oats
Low-sugar natural granola
Gluten-free graham crackers
Corn tortillas
Corn tortilla chips
Rice cakes

SEEDS, NUTS, & BEANS

Chia seeds (Healthworks Raw Chia Seeds)
Milled flax seeds (Spectrum Essentials Organic Ground Flaxseed)
Hemp seeds (Manitoba Harvest Natural Hemp Hearts Raw Shelled Hemp Seeds)
Lightly salted sunflower seeds
Pumpkin seeds
Peanuts
Cashews
Almonds
Pecans
Walnuts
Canned black beans
Canned chickpeas

FRUIT

Blueberries
Blackberries
Raspberries
Mangoes
Bananas
Grapes
Pineapples
Lemons
Limes
Apples
No-sugar-added frozen fruits (variety of fresh fruit listed above)
No-sugar-added dried cranberries

VEGETABLES

Spinach
Kale
Lettuce
Avocados
Peppers (green, red, yellow)
Red and yellow onions
Green onions
Garlic
Carrots
Sprouts (alfalfa, broccoli, bean)
Cucumbers
Tomatoes
Mushrooms
Celery
Broccoli slaw
Cauliflower
Peas (fresh or frozen)
Jalapeños
Asparagus
Zucchini
Spaghetti squash
Acorn squash
Sweet potatoes
Radishes

If you stick to these lists, and leave the processed junk on the shelf, you will eat healthy, feel great, and take those first concrete steps from settling to thriving. Notice that even chocolate and cheese are on this list, so you can celebrate your new lifestyle with a sampler served with a glass of pinot noir. A diet would make you forget the wine, chocolate, cheese, and pretty much everything else delicious.

LUCKILY THIS ISN'T A DIET. IT'S THE BEGINNING OF A NEW LIFE AND THE BEGINNING OF A NEW YOU.

CHAPTER TWELVE

YOU MADE IT! IT'S TIME TO START THRIVING... AND EATING!

If you're new to the whole gluten-free/healthy eating thing, don't stress. I got you. There are 50 recipes in this book to get you started. They're all super easy, take 30 minutes or less to make, and taste amazeballs. Best of all, you don't need to be a 5-star chef. Lord knows I'm not.

Before we start cooking, I want to congratulate you for actually reading this entire book! You made a promise, you stuck to it, and now you're better for it. If you didn't, come on. Go back and read the book. Do it now.

Back to the people who read this book. Thank you; you're amazing! You now have the tools and knowledge about nutrition to confidently begin your new healthy lifestyle. This is the new you moving forward. No more diets, quick fixes, or 5-day eating binges. You're better than that. You're a cashmere sweater, not some low-grade knock-off, remember? Let's also remember that best-case scenario we talked about at the beginning of this book.

Imagine it's 6 months from now. You're trying on bathing suits at Victoria's Secret, and you make sure to pick out the sexiest ones you can find (which you NEVER would have done before). You try them on, look in the mirror, and are overwhelmed by what you see. It happened. You've done it. You've changed your life. Your ab muscles are smiling back at you, your energy levels are sky-high, your confidence is through the roof, and you look damn good in that bikini. You're thriving and it never felt so good.

NOW IT'S TIME TO MAKE IT HAPPEN. LET'S GET COOKING!

Part Four:
RECIPES

BREAKFAST

Remember when your mom would yell before school, "Make sure you eat your breakfast! It's the most important meal of the day!"? Well, she was right. Breakfast should never be skipped. It should also not be treated like the half-eaten cream-filled donut that got smashed on your way to work.

What you eat for breakfast **will** set the tone for the rest of your day. If you eat a bowl of sugary, processed cereal or a bagel smothered in cream cheese with a large, sugar-filled Chai latte, both your day and you will need a pick-me-up before lunch even starts. If you don't eat anything because you want to "cut calories," within an hour you will: 1. Be hungry 2. Be really really hungry 3. Not be able to focus on anything besides what you brought for lunch, and 4. Grab the first thing you see and demolish it. So much for "cutting those calories."

Think about this: By the time you wake up, most likely, you haven't eaten for 10+ hours. If you skip breakfast, you're most likely not eating for 15+ hours. That's more than half of a day without eating! Skipping breakfast trains your body to go into starvation mode because it's not sure when it's going to get fed again. When your body goes into starvation mode, fat is stored instead of burned to use later as an energy source. Why? Because your body's number one priority is to protect itself. When you don't eat for extended periods of time, your body protects itself by storing fat to survive. So when you skip breakfast, you're essentially training your body to store your next meal as fat. Do you want your body to store fat? No. So eat your damn breakfast.

I know, mornings are hard, and you're lucky to even grab a granola bar as you rush out the door. However, with a little planning, breakfast can be quick, easy, and nutrient-packed. That's the way it should be. Would you rather start your day on the wrong foot because you ate a bunch of processed, empty calories? Or would you rather thrive because you ate food that's actually good for you? Thrive, of course. So let's get cracking... eggs.

Mixed Berry Protein
PANCAKES

START TO FINISH: **20 MINUTES**

SERVINGS: **2**

+ 2 Tbsp. natural peanut butter+ ½ cup fresh berries

1 ½ cups plain nonfat Greek yogurt

½ cup berries of your choice

2 large eggs

1 scoop vanilla protein powder (20g of protein per scoop)

¼ cup gluten-free flour (I use coconut flour)

2 Tbsp. of unsweetened dairy-free milk (add up to ¼ cup milk if you prefer thinner pancakes)

1 tsp. baking soda

1 Tbsp. coconut oil for greasing the pan

TOPPINGS/SERVING

2 Tbsp. natural peanut butter

½ cup fresh berries

MACROS/SERVING

Calories: 469

Protein: 40.4g

Total Fats: 23.1g

Saturated Fat: 8.5g

Carbs: 28.1g

Sugars: 11g

Fiber: 5.8g

Don't let 23 grams of fat and 40 grams of protein scare you away from this recipe. You will regret it; trust me. These pancakes are packed with nutrition, are low-sugar, and are ridiculously delicious. Make them by the dozen and keep them on supply in your freezer.

My recommendation: Eat them before or after an intense workout. The protein is vital for feeding your muscles and the carbs will give you some pep in your step.

ADD all the pancake ingredients into a food processor or blender and mix on low/medium speed until it's smooth. Add in additional milk if you prefer thinner pancakes.

COAT a medium-sized pan with 1 Tbsp. of coconut oil on medium heat. Pour the batter into the pan, forming 3–4 inch circles. Flip after 1–2 minutes when bubbles start to form. Cook both sides to your liking.

SERVE them immediately with fresh berries and nut butter.

PRO TIP:
Cook the pancakes with a lid to get them perfectly golden brown.

Mini Cottage Cheese Protein
PANCAKES

START TO FINISH: 20–25 MINUTES

SERVINGS: 2

> 3-4 mini-pancakes per serving
> + 1 Tbsp. honey
> + ½ cup fresh fruit

1 cup fat-free cottage cheese

¾ cup rolled oats

2 large eggs

1 tsp. vanilla extract

3 Tbsp. hemp seeds (you can swap these for chia seeds)

1 tsp. baking powder

½ tsp. cinnamon

1 pinch of salt

1 Tbsp. coconut oil (use this throughout to coat the pan while cooking)

TOPPINGS/SERVING

1 Tbsp. honey

½ cup fresh fruit

MACROS/SERVING

Calories: 421

Protein: 27.6g

Total Fat: 18.9g

Saturated Fat: 8.2g

Carbs: 33.7g

Sugars: 13.6g

Fiber: 1.8g

Ever heard of a cheese blintz? If yes, your mouth is probably watering already. Well these pancakes are the healthy (but still tasty) version. The cottage cheese makes these pancakes moist, while packing them with protein without adding fat. Hemp seeds give these pancakes a healthy dose of omega-3 and omega-6 fatty acids, protein, and fiber. Don't have hemp seeds? Use chia seeds instead!

PULSE together all of the ingredients, except for the coconut oil, in a blender or food processor until they are combined. It should look a little lumpy.

HEAT a large pan or skillet (or 2 pans or skillets if you are short on time) over medium heat and add ½ Tbsp. of coconut oil. Swirl it around to grease the pan.

POUR the batter into the pan to form 2–4 mini-pancakes. This will differ depending on the size of your pan. Place the lid on top of the pan.

COOK the pancakes for 1–2 minutes until little bubbles form on the top and they're golden brown on the bottom.

FLIP the pancakes and cook them for another 1–2 minutes or until the bottom is golden brown.

REMOVE the pancakes from the pan and transfer them to a serving plate. Repeat this with the remaining batter, continuing to grease the pan.

SERVE the pancakes with honey and fresh fruit.

Peanut Butter Banana
PROTEIN MUFFINS

START TO FINISH: 20 MINUTES

SERVINGS: MAKES 6 MUFFINS

1 muffin per serving

1 ripe banana, mashed

2 Tbsp. natural peanut butter

¼ cup rolled oats (uncooked)

1 whole egg

½ cup egg whites

1 scoop vanilla protein powder (20g of protein per scoop)

2 Tbsp. chia seeds

1 tsp. baking powder

½ tsp. vanilla extract

MACROS/SERVING

Calories: 124

Protein: 9g

Total Fat: 5.1g

Saturated Fat: 0.7g

Carbs: 11.8g

Sugars: 2.7g

Fiber: 3.3g

These muffins are my ramped-up version of Trader Joe's Protein Power Banana Chocolate Chip Muffins. In college, I ate these in bulk. It was my normal, go-to, quick breakfast as I ran out the door to catch the 8:00 AM shuttle to class. When I learned how to cook, I realized I could make these muffins healthier without sacrificing taste. Three rounds of muffin disasters later, this delicious recipe was born! These muffins have almost zero sugar, are high in protein, and will make your mouth water. Want to make them into a healthy dessert? Add ¼ cup of dark chocolate chips to the recipe.

My recommendation: Make a double batch and keep extra muffins in the fridge or freezer for a quick breakfast or snack on-the-go. If they are being kept in the fridge, the muffins will stay fresh for up to 7 days.

PREHEAT the oven to 350°F.

MIX all of the ingredients together in a medium-sized bowl.

PLACE the mixture into a pre-greased muffin tin.

BAKE for 15 minutes until they are golden brown.

NOTES:

Peanut butter can be swapped out for other nut butters, including almond butter, sunflower butter, and cashew butter. If you have a nut allergy, add an extra ½ of a banana to replace the peanut butter.

"PB&J" Oatmeal

START TO FINISH: 5 MINUTES

SERVINGS: 1

⅓ cup rolled oats

A little more than ½ cup unsweetened dairy-free milk

1 Tbsp. chia seeds

2 Tbsp. milled flax seeds

1 Tbsp. peanut butter (or other nut butter)

½ cup of fresh blueberries

MACROS/SERVING

Calories: 371

Protein: 13.1g

Total Fat: 18.3g

Saturated Fat: 1.8g

Carbs: 39.7g

Sugars: 9.2g

Fiber: 13.6g

Out of every breakfast recipe in this book, I hands-down eat this one the most. The way I see it, oatmeal should be a staple in everyone's diet. It's loaded with healthy complex carbs that keep you full, and provides you with energy to start your day with a BANG. Peanut butter adds creaminess and protein. Blueberries add sweetness and fiber. This oatmeal is like eating dessert for breakfast, but without the guilt and extra pounds. Win/win!

MIX all of the ingredients together, except the blueberries, in a microwave safe bowl.

PLACE the bowl in the microwave for 1 minute and 30 seconds to 2 minutes. Top the mixture with fresh berries and cinnamon.

NOTES:

If you have a nut allergy, replace the peanut butter with ½ scoop of protein powder.

PIÑA COLADA
Overnight Oats

START TO FINISH: 5 MINUTES TO PREP + 4–5 HOURS IN THE FRIDGE

SERVINGS: 1

¼ cup plain nonfat Greek yogurt

¼ cup rolled oats

⅓ cup coconut milk, or unsweetened dairy-free milk

1 Tbsp. chia seeds

1 Tbsp. milled flax seeds

½ tsp. vanilla extract

½ cup chopped fresh or frozen no-sugar-added pineapple (mango tastes great too!)

½ ripe banana, chopped or mashed

2 Tbsp. unsweetened flaked coconut

MACROS/SERVING

Calories: 394

Protein: 12.8g

Total Fat: 14.5g

Saturated Fat: 6.9g

Carbs: 54.9g

Sugars: 25.8g

Fiber: 11.9g

Overnight oats are one of my favorite summertime breakfast recipes. They're served cold, which is extremely refreshing when it's 90 degrees outside. Just like my PB&J oatmeal recipe, overnight oats are loaded with healthy complex carbs and fiber, which ward off mindless snack cravings.

Know that you're going to have a really busy week? Prep a few servings in advance and store them in mason jars in the fridge for an easy grab-and-go breakfast!

My recommendation: Get creative with this recipe! This is just one of my favorite versions, but the pineapple can easily be replaced with blueberries, strawberries, apples, or any fruit you have on hand.

MIX together all of the ingredients, except for the coconut flakes, in a medium-sized mixing bowl. Spoon it into a jar with a tight-fitting lid (I love mason jars!).

REFRIGERATE for at least 4 hours, but preferably overnight, before eating. Top with the coconut flakes and serve it cold.

NOTES:

Store the overnight oats for up to one week in the fridge. Check the expiration date of your milk and yogurt, and add the coconut flake topping the day you enjoy your oats to ensure that they don't get soggy.

Vanilla Chia Seed
PROTEIN PUDDING

START TO FINISH: 5 MINUTES TO PREP + 20–30 MINUTES IN THE FRIDGE

SERVINGS: 2

1 pudding + ½ cup fresh berries per serving

4 Tbsp. chia seeds

1½ cups unsweetened dairy-free milk

1 scoop vanilla protein powder (20g of protein per scoop)

½ tsp. cinnamon

½ cup fresh berries (or fruit of your choice) per serving

MACROS/SERVING

Calories: 221

Protein: 14.9g

Total Fat: 10.5g

Saturated Fat: 0.7g

Carbs: 20.9g

Sugars: 0.5g

Fiber: 12.9g

Pudding for breakfast? Yes! Now there's something to get out of bed for. This recipe has all the sweetness of regular pudding minus the sugar. Chia seeds pack this dish with fiber and a heart-healthy dose of omega-3 fatty acids. Cinnamon helps reduce inflammation and is loaded with antioxidants; it is also known as the natural version of botox. Just like the overnight oats recipe, get creative by adding your favorite toppings like blueberries, coconut flakes, cacao nibs, or nuts! This recipe is also great served as a snack or late-night dessert since it's low in carbs and sugar!

My recommendation: Make a few versions of this recipe in advance and store them in individual mason jars to eat throughout the week.

ADD chia seeds, milk, cinnamon, and protein powder into two resealable storage containers (split the ingredients evenly), such as mason jars. Mix until combined.

PLACE the pudding in the refrigerator for 20–30 minutes, or store it overnight.

SERVE with ½ cup fresh berries or fruit of your choice.

Mixed Berry
PROTEIN SMOOTHIE

START TO FINISH: **LESS THAN 5 MINUTES**

SERVINGS: **1**

½ cup frozen mixed berries (fresh berries can be used as well)

1 big handful of spinach

1 scoop chocolate or vanilla protein powder (20g of protein per scoop)

½ cup of unsweetened dairy-free milk or water

2-3 ice cubes

MACROS/SERVING

Calories: 204

Protein: 22.4g

Total Fat: 4.8g

Saturated Fat: 0.0g

Carbs: 24g

Sugars: 6.1g

Fiber: 7.8g

If you barely have time to eat breakfast before work, let alone take a lunch break, smoothies are your new best friend. They take less than five minutes to make, are portable, and can be consumed at your desk without missing a keystroke. Protein smoothies are great as a quick breakfast, but also as a quick protein source after a hard workout (Remember, you need to eat protein within 30 minutes of exercise!). They are also dummy-proof. Just blend a bunch of fruits and veggies together with protein powder, and you have a healthy and tasty meal or snack.

My recommendation: Prepare your smoothie the night before by storing the ingredients in an airtight container. Blend the ingredients together in the morning and go! Are you starting to get the theme of this book? Prep as much as you can in advance and eat healthy and stress-free every day of the week.

PLACE all of the ingredients in a blender.

BLEND them and serve cold.

NOTES:

If you're really watching your calories and carbs, opt for water instead of milk.

CALIFORNIA FRIED EGG
with Avocado Toast

START TO FINISH: 7 MINUTES
SERVINGS: 1

1 slice gluten-free bread, toasted
1 small handful of fresh spinach
¼ medium ripe avocado, sliced thin
2 tomato slices
¼ small red onion, sliced thin
½ Tbsp. olive oil
2 large eggs
1 Tbsp. minced fresh cilantro
Salt and pepper to taste

MACROS/SERVING

Calories: 357.6
Protein: 19.0g
Total Fat: 19.4g
Saturated Fat: 4.5g
Carbs: 28.8g
Sugars: 1.6g
Fiber: 8.1g

Eggs are the one of the quickest and cheapest protein sources known to man. They are also delicious. The crunch from the toast paired with the creaminess of the avocado transforms this simple egg recipe into a mouthwatering delight. For you cilantro lovers, add a dash on top for a flavor explosion in your mouth.

TOP the toast with the spinach, avocado, tomato and red onion slices. Set aside.

HEAT the oil in a medium-sized saucepan over medium-high heat. Crack 2 eggs into the pan and sprinkle with salt and pepper.

COVER the pan with the lid and allow the eggs to cook without flipping them until the egg whites are set. Carefully remove the eggs from the pan with a spatula and transfer them to a plate.

ARRANGE the fried eggs on top of the toast. Sprinkle with minced cilantro and eat hot.

PRO TIP:
Cook the eggs sunny-side up without breaking the yolk by covering the pan with a lid. The eggs will cook perfectly without needing to be flipped, reducing the risk of cracking the yolk.

Mediterranean FRITTATA

START TO FINISH: **30 MINUTES**

SERVINGS: **4**

¼ frittata per serving

8 links of nitrate-free, uncured, fully-cooked turkey sausage, diced

3 large eggs + 5 egg whites, lightly beaten

¼ cup feta cheese

Salt and pepper to taste

2 cups fresh spinach, loosely measured

1 medium tomato, diced small

½ small white onion, diced

1 Tbsp. olive oil

MACROS/SERVING

Calories: 217

Protein: 20.6g

Total Fat: 12.5g

Saturated Fat: 3.7g

Carbs: 6.1g

Sugars: 0.5g

Fiber: 1g

PRO TIP:

Make this recipe in advance and reheat it throughout the week in the microwave for 2 minutes. After cooking it, store it in an airtight container in the fridge for up to one week.

Frittatas are one of those make-ahead recipes that can never go wrong. They are also perfect for brunch when you need to feed a group on a budget. Just like a smoothie, you can use whatever you have available to make this dish. Some of my favorite add-ins include mushrooms, zucchini, peppers, olives, and leftover chicken. If you're vegetarian, simply take out the meat. If feta messes with your stomach, take out the cheese. You can't really mess this up, so get creative!

My recommendation: Splurge on nitrate-free, uncured meat. It tastes better, and is better for you. Why? Cured meats are jam-packed with preservatives called nitrates. Studies show that nitrates can increase your chance of getting cancer[3]. That's a big enough reason for me to pay an extra $3 for bacon.

PREHEAT the oven to 400°F.

WHISK together the eggs and egg whites in a medium-sized bowl. Set them aside.

HEAT a nonstick pan with the olive oil over medium-high heat.

ADD the onion, cooking for 2–3 minutes until it is fragrant, and then add the turkey sausage, tomatoes, and any additional produce to the pan (see suggestions below), cooking for an additional 2 minutes. Add the spinach and cook until it wilts slightly; about 30 seconds.

TRANSFER the pan mixture into a baking dish coated with olive oil, draining as much liquid as possible.

ADD the whisked eggs and feta cheese. Place aluminum foil over the dish and bake it for 10 minutes.

REMOVE the foil and bake the dish for an additional 4–6 minutes, until the center is ALMOST set. The eggs will continue to cook while it is cooling.

COOL the dish for 5–10 minutes. Serve it warm.

[3] http://www.cancercenter.com/discussions/blog/the-link-between-sodium-nitrites-and-cancer/

Skinny Greek
OMELET

START TO FINISH: 10 MINUTES

SERVINGS: 1

2 large eggs + 1 egg white, beaten

½ tsp. olive oil

2 Tbsp. red onion, diced

½ Roma tomato or tomato of your choice, diced

1 cup spinach

3–5 basil leafs, chopped

1 Tbsp. feta cheese

Salt and pepper to taste

MACROS/SERVING

Calories: 258

Protein: 19.7g

Total Fat: 16.6g

Saturated Fat: 4.9g

Carbs: 8.3g

Sugars: 4.1g

Fiber: 2g

Combining egg whites with whole eggs is a tasty way to get your protein without feeling like you're eating cardboard. I have been making omelets like this for years and I am obsessed. Throw in a little feta cheese, tomato, and onion, and you've got yourself a satisfying breakfast that's loaded with nutrition and flavor. As mentioned before, cut out the feta if dairy upsets your stomach. And always remember to get creative, adding in your favorite veggies.

HEAT a small skillet (6-inch) over medium-low heat. Add the oil, onion, tomato, and spinach and cook them for about 2 minutes, until the onions soften and the spinach has wilted. Set aside.

COAT the skillet with olive oil and add the beaten eggs. Season them with salt and pepper. Allow the eggs to set for about 30 seconds.

LOOSEN the edges of the omelet with a spatula, tilting the skillet and allowing the uncooked eggs to run down the skillet walls.

REPEAT this action until the eggs are almost cooked for 2–3 minutes.

ADD the cooked vegetables, feta cheese, and basil to one side of the omelet. Fold the omelet in half and cook it for an additional minute until the cheese is melted and the omelet isn't runny.

SLIDE the omelet onto a plate and serve it immediately.

SNACKS

What are the first foods that come to mind when you think of "snacks"? Typically, foods like granola bars, chips, crackers, cookies, yogurt, and cheese. These foods, while tempting, can be a problem if you're trying to live a healthy lifestyle. Almost all of these foods are processed and loaded with sugar. They're also lacking in the nutrient department, and barely contain enough complex carbs and protein to feed a small animal. Are you a small animal? No. Then why would you eat like one? Ideally, you wouldn't.

What's the secret to creating fresh and satisfying snacks? The secret is pairing a complex carb with a protein. For example, an apple with peanut butter. Paired together, this food combo creates a snack that will intrigue your taste buds and keep you full until your next meal. Why? Remember what we learned in Chapter 4 about pairing protein sources? If you don't, go back and read that section again. Yes, seriously.

We're going to make these "ideal" snacks the norm with a little planning. When planning your snacks, I suggest preparing 1–2 recipes with larger serving sizes (serves 4 or more) at the beginning of the week. If you're running low on snacks, add in a few single-serve snacks (serves 1) as needed. This means a little more planning, but a little goes a long way when you want something other than that boring, pre-packaged granola bar. So toss aside that bag of chips and let's get snacking!

Healthy Cranberry
BLISS BARS

START TO FINISH: 25 MINUTES
SERVINGS: MAKES 9 BARS

1 bar per serving

2 ripe bananas

⅓ cup applesauce

1 cup quick-cooking oats

2 scoops vanilla protein powder (20g of protein per scoop)

¼ cup unsweetened vanilla dairy-free milk

¼ cup no-sugar-added dried cranberries

4 Tbsp. chia seeds

4 Tbsp. milled flax seeds

1 tsp. cinnamon

1 tsp. vanilla extract

1 Tbsp. honey

MACROS/SERVING

Calories: 161

Protein: 8.5g

Total Fat: 5.4g

Saturated Fat: 0.5g

Carbs: 25.2g

Sugars: 8.9g

Fiber: 6.8g

These bars were inspired by Starbucks' famous Cranberry Bliss Bars. The original Starbucks recipe contains a whopping 300 calories, 15 grams of fat (9 grams of which is saturated), and 26 grams of sugar per bar. Holy heart attack on a plate! This recipe slashes these artery-clogging numbers in half while adding 8.5 grams of protein and 6.8 grams of fiber. Eat one with a black coffee. Ah, true bliss.

PREHEAT the oven to 350°F. In a medium-sized bowl, mash the bananas with a fork or potato masher. Add the rest of the ingredients and mix them well.

TRANSFER the mixture into a greased 8x8" pan and top it with extra cinnamon if desired. Bake it for 20 minutes or until the edges are golden brown.

COOL and cut it into nine bars. Store them in individual bags or plastic wrap in the fridge until they are ready to be eaten.

NOTES:

These bars stay fresh in the fridge for up to 1 week. If you choose to freeze them, thaw them by placing them in the fridge a day in advance. They can also be thawed by popping them in the microwave for 1 minute and 30 seconds.

Chocolate Peanut Butter
ENERGY BALLS

START TO FINISH: 10 MINUTES

SERVINGS: MAKES 12 BALLS

1 ball per serving

⅔ cup + 1 Tbsp. creamy natural peanut butter

2 Tbsp. unsweetened dairy-free milk

⅓ cup dark chocolate chips (I use the mini-chips)

1 cup old-fashioned oats

½ cup milled flax seeds

2 Tbsp. honey

MACROS/SERVING

Calories: 178

Protein: 5.3g

Total Fat: 11.6g

Saturated Fat: 3.1g

Carbs: 15.6g

Sugars: 7.4g

Fiber: 3.4g

This is the perfect snack to grab when you're in a rush. It's filling due to the complex carbs from the oats and protein-packed peanut butter, and is much more satisfying than the store-bought granola bar. It's better for you too!

PLACE all of the ingredients into a medium-sized bowl. Stir them until all of the ingredients are combined.

ROLL the mixture into 12, 1-inch balls and store them in the fridge for up to a week.

NOTES:

If your mixture is too dry to stick together, add a little more milk.

Greek Yogurt
GARLIC & DILL DIP

START TO FINISH: 5 MINUTES

SERVINGS: 4

½ cup per serving
+ 1 cup raw veggies

2 cups plain nonfat Greek yogurt

8 sprigs of fresh dill, chopped with stems removed

2 garlic cloves, minced

1 lemon, juiced

Pinch of salt to taste

1 cup raw veggies per serving

MACROS/SERVING

Calories: 91

Protein: 12.2g

Total Fat: 2g

Saturated Fat: 0.3g

Carbs: 8g

Sugars: 6g

Fiber: 0.8g

This dip is perfect to bring to a party or social gathering. Unlike the standard party dip that's loaded with saturated fat, this dip only contains 2 grams of fat per serving, and is still packed with flavor. It also only takes 5 minutes to make. You can now jump for joy.

My recommendation: If you are attending a party, make a double batch and serve it with a tray of fresh veggies. Otherwise, enjoy a single serving as a snack before lunch.

COMBINE the yogurt with the chopped dill, minced garlic, lemon juice, and salt in a small bowl.

LET the dip sit in the fridge for about 5 minutes. This will allow the flavors to marinate.

SERVE with one cup of fresh veggies, such as cucumbers, snap peas, carrots, and peppers.

FRESH BLACK BEAN DIP
with Veggies

START TO FINISH: **5 MINUTES**

SERVINGS: **6**

> ¼ cup per serving
> + 1 cup raw veggies

1 can low-sodium black beans, drained & rinsed

¼ cup salsa

1 garlic clove, minced

½ red onion, chopped

1 lime, juiced

½ tsp. ground cumin

1 tsp. water

Pinch of salt

2 Tbsp. cilantro, minced

1 cup of raw veggies per serving

MACROS/SERVING

Calories: 96

Protein: 5.3g

Total Fat: 1.7g

Saturated Fat: 0.2g

Carbs: 18.8g

Sugars: 1.6g

Fiber: 4.9g

This flavorful dip is a twist on the standard chips and salsa favorite. It tastes great served with fresh peppers, corn tortilla chips, or over eggs!

PUREE all the ingredients except the veggies in a food processor or blender until the mixture is smooth.

SERVE with 1 cup of raw veggies.

MANGO AVOCADO SALSA
with Corn Tortilla Chips

START TO FINISH: **7 MINUTES**

SERVINGS: **4**

> about ½ cup per serving + 1 handful of corn tortilla chips (9-11 chips)

2 medium-large ripe mangos; peeled, pitted, and cubed

1 medium-large avocado; peeled, pitted, and cubed

¼ red onion, diced

2–3 Tbsp. cilantro, chopped

2 limes, juiced

¼ tsp. salt

1 handful corn tortilla chips (9—11 chips) per serving

MACROS/SERVING

Calories: 280

Protein: 3.2g

Total Fat: 14.5g

Saturated Fat: 1.0g

Carbs: 41.7g

Sugars: 15.8g

Fiber: 6.7g

Mango and avocado is the best combination since peanut butter and jelly. The sweetness of the mango pairs perfectly with savory meats, such as pork, grilled chicken, and white fish. The creamy, fresh avocado adds balance to the salsa. Want to spice up a boring salad? Throw this in! This salsa can turn almost any bland dish into a work of art. Just try to not eat the whole thing in one sitting.

COMBINE the mango, avocado, red onion, and cilantro in a bowl.

ADD the lime juice and salt. Mix them well.

SERVE the dish with one handful of corn tortilla chips (9—11 chips).

Protein-Packed
TOAST

START TO FINISH: 5 MINUTES
SERVINGS: 1

1 slice gluten-free bread, toasted
1 Tbsp. hummus
½ cup alfalfa sprouts
1 hard-boiled egg, sliced

MACROS/SERVING

Calories: 186
Protein: 11g
Total Fat: 8.8g
Saturated Fat: 1.8g
Carbs: 21.2g
Sugars: 1.6g
Fiber: 6.3g

Finally, a snack with bread! Don't get too excited, it's still gluten-free. On a serious note, this snack packs in a satisfying 11 grams protein. AKA why it's named "protein-packed toast". Eat this between meals, for lunch, or for breakfast. It's great any time of the day, so eat up!

LAYER the toast with the hummus, the sprouts, and the hard-boiled egg slices. Eat it immediately.

APPLE

With Nut Butter

START TO FINISH: **LESS THAN 5 MINUTES**

SERVINGS: **1**

1 medium-large apple, cored and sliced

1 Tbsp. peanut butter or other nut butter

1 Tbsp. hemp seeds

MACROS/SERVING

Calories: 218

Protein: 7.7g

Total Fat: 11.6g

Saturated Fat: 1.5g

Carbs: 23.1g

Sugars: 15.7g

Fiber: 5.3g

Everyone loves an apple with peanut butter. It's a classic snack that tastes more like a treat without the guilt! To add more protein and fiber to this snack without smothering your apple with peanut butter, sprinkle hemp seeds, chia seeds, or flax seeds on top.

DRIZZLE the peanut butter over the sliced apple. Top it with hemp seeds. Eat it immediately.

Fruit & Yogurt
PARFAIT

START TO FINISH: LESS THAN 5 MINUTES

SERVINGS: 1

1 cup plain nonfat Greek yogurt

⅓ cup whole-grain low-sugar granola (less than 15 grams of sugar per serving)

½ cup fresh berries

MACROS/SERVING

Calories: 313

Protein: 27.5g

Total Fat: 2.9g

Saturated Fat: 0.0g

Carbs: 45.2g

Sugars: 18g

Fiber: 6.5g

This recipe is great as a snack or as a quick and healthy breakfast! Depending on the time of year, eat it with fresh, seasonal fruit instead of berries.

SPOON the yogurt into a bowl and top it with the granola and fresh berries. Eat it immediately.

Cottage Cheese
DELIGHT

START TO FINISH: LESS THAN 5 MINUTES

SERVINGS: 1

½ cup fat-free cottage cheese

1 Tbsp. slivered almonds

½ cup fresh berries

MACROS/SERVING

Calories: 192

Protein: 19.5g

Total Fat: 8g

Saturated Fat: 0.5g

Carbs: 15.5g

Sugars: 3g

Fiber: 4g

Cottage cheese is one of those super healthy foods that flies under the radar. Not only is cottage cheese a great protein source, but it's light on carbs, sugar, and fat (if you buy 1% or fat-free). Nuts add extra protein and crunch to this dish, making it seem like a guilt-free treat when paired with fruit. Mix up this recipe by swapping out almonds for walnuts, pecans, and cashews.

SPOON the cottage cheese into a bowl. Top it with almonds and fresh berries. Eat immediately.

SALT & VINEGAR KALE CHIPS
with Hard-Boiled Eggs

START TO FINISH: 15 MINUTES
SERVINGS: 2

½ the kale chips
+ 1 egg per serving

1 bunch of kale
2 Tbsp. apple cider vinegar
1 Tbsp. olive oil
½ tsp. coarse sea salt, more/less to taste
2 hard-boiled eggs; 1 per serving

MACROS/SERVING

Calories: 171
Protein: 8.5g
Total Fat: 12.6g
Saturated Fat: 2.6g
Carbs: 7.3g
Sugars: 0.6g
Fiber: 1.3g

Crispy and tasty, kale chips are the next best thing to regular chips. They're loaded with vitamins and nutrients instead of processed junk. You may be wondering where the eggs come into play. Well, as I keep stressing, all meals should contain a protein source so you're not starving within 30 minutes. Serving this dish with hard-boiled eggs adds protein, making this a complete and filling snack.

PREHEAT the oven to 400°F.

WASH and dry the kale leaves. Using a knife, separate the green kale leaves from the thick ribs and discard the ribs. Cut or tear the kale leaves into your desired size of chips, knowing that they will shrink a bit while baking.

COMBINE the kale leaves, vinegar, oil and ¼ tsp of salt in a large bowl. Toss all of the ingredients together until they are coated evenly.

SPREAD the kale in a single layer on a baking sheet (or two). Sprinkle with the remaining salt.

BAKE the kale for 10 minutes or until the kale is crunchy and no longer soft. Remove the kale chips from the oven and serve them immediately with one hard-boiled egg.

NOTES:

Kale chips are best eaten immediately. However, if you have leftovers, store them in a sealed container for up to 5 days. To reheat them, sauté the chips in a pan over medium heat for 2 minutes until hot and crispy.

Tuna Avocado
BITES

START TO FINISH: 7 MINUTES

SERVINGS: 2

½ filled avocado per serving
1 handful celery sticks

1 avocado, cut in half, pit removed, diced, skins reserved

1, 5-oz. can white Albacore tuna in water, water drained

½ tomato, diced, about 3 Tbsp.

2 Tbsp. red onion, diced

Small handful of parsley, chopped, about 2 Tbsp.

½ lime, juiced

Salt and pepper to taste

1 handfull celery sticks per serving

MACROS/SERVING

Calories: 242.3

Protein: 18.2g

Total Fat: 14.3g

Saturated Fat: 2.4g

Carbs: 14.5g

Sugars: 0.8g

Fiber: 8.5g

Canned tuna is one of the most boring protein sources on the planet. Besides tuna salad or tuna casserole, there aren't many exciting options. In an effort to dress up canned tuna, this recipe was born. Not only are these tuna avocado bites delicious, but they look like a Pinterest cover photo when served in the avocado skin. Bring these to a dinner party and watch as everyone's jaws drop and mouths water. They're always a hit, and it doesn't hurt that they take less than 10 minutes to make.

COMBINE all the ingredients in a small bowl and mix them together with a fork. Really smash the avocado to break it up.

DIVIDE the mixture between the 2 avocado skins and serve with celery sticks.

NOTES:

If you don't have a red onion, use chopped celery instead for an added crunch.

LUNCH & DINNER

Do your lunches and dinners frequently come with a, "Thank you; come again!" from the Chinese takeout restaurant down the street? Or the other extreme: A dry chicken breast served with a side of tasteless veggies? Both sound horrible. Never eat either again.

Moving forward, lunches will be prepped and full of flavor; dinners will be masterfully crafted in the blink of an eye; and everyone will have a full stomach and a thinner waist. Sounds great, right?

This is not something you find at the end of the rainbow (or some other mythical reference), but it's what we will achieve today, together.

In order to get here, these meals need to be planned and prepped. Yes, we're going back to that "planning thing." It's really not that hard; I promise. To set you up for success, I put in the leg-work to create a plan to help you plan.

(continued on page 118)

THE DUMMY-PROOF PLAN FOR MAKING BANGIN, ASS LUNCHES AND DINNERS

Pick 1 day a week to prepare 1–2 larger meals (meals that serve 4 or more). Let's pick Sunday. These two recipes should make you about 8 lunch and dinner meals and hypothetically keep you fed through Thursday night. If you're cooking for more than yourself, add in one more larger meal and/or add in smaller meals throughout the week.

Make double batches of easy-to-freeze recipes and eat them when needed. This will add variety to your meals and save you from becoming a slave to the kitchen. Fortunately, if you missed your meal prep day, these recipes all take 30 minutes or less to make. The more you prep, the less you need to cook, and the more you can enjoy life.

These recipes are meant to give you sustained energy and keep you full until your next meal. Each meal includes a protein source paired with a veggie, carb, or both. Depending on what your macro count is by lunch or dinner, plan your meals accordingly. For example, if you're almost at your recommended carbohydrate intake by dinner, choose a meal that's lower in carbs, or swap the primary carbohydrate source for mixed greens or cauliflower rice. Got it? Good. Let's make some bangin, ass meals!

LEMON & HERB
SPAGHETTI SQUASH
with Shrimp

START TO FINISH: 30 MINUTES
SERVINGS: 4

> 2 cups spaghetti squash
> + 5 shrimp per serving

1 medium-large spaghetti squash

12 oz. large frozen shrimp, thawed (about 20 shrimp, peeled and deveined)

1 Tbsp. olive oil

Salt and pepper, to taste

2-3 garlic cloves, minced

1 lemon, juiced

½ cup dry white wine or white wine vinegar

1 tsp. dijon mustard

¼ tsp. red pepper flakes

¼ cup plain nonfat Greek yogurt

2 Tbsp. fresh parsley, chopped

2 Tbsp. fresh capers (optional)

MACROS/SERVING

Calories: 207

Protein: 20.8g

Total Fat: 4.4g

Saturated Fat: 0.7g

Carbs: 23.6g

Sugars: 9g

Fiber: 5.6g

I LOVE spaghetti squash! It's like eating pasta, but without the added carbs. Better yet, you can fill your entire plate to the brim, and it will barely make a dent in your macro count. Placing the spaghetti squash in the microwave instead of the oven shaves off more than 45 minutes of cooking time. Technology really is amazing.

In fact, the hardest part of this recipe is cutting the spaghetti squash in half. Make sure you use a sharp knife and are prepared for a fight, because it will fight back. Consider it your workout for the day.

CUT the spaghetti squash in half lengthwise and cut off the stem. Scoop out the seeds with a spoon.

PLACE spaghetti squash cut-side-down in a microwave-safe dish at least 1 inch tall. Fill the dish with ½ inch of water. Microwave spaghetti squash on high for 10 minutes.

MELT the oil over medium-high heat in a large skillet. Add the shrimp and season them with salt and pepper, sautéing them for about 2 minutes. Add the garlic and sauté this for an additional 2 minutes until the shrimp is cooked through. Remove everything from the heat and set it aside (you don't want to overcook the shrimp).

ADD lemon juice, white wine, dijon mustard, and red pepper flakes into the skillet. Bring this to a boil. Reduce the heat and allow the sauce to simmer for 5 minutes.

REMOVE the spaghetti squash from microwave (you should be able to easily poke it with a fork). Scrape out the strands of "spaghetti" using a fork. Place the spaghetti squash into a colander. Drain any excess water in the squash by pressing gently with a paper or kitchen towel.

WHISK the plain nonfat Greek yogurt in with the sauce until the mixture is creamy and smooth. Stir in the chopped parsley and capers. Toss this with the spaghetti squash and shrimp. Serve it immediately.

PRO TIP:
When preparing the spaghetti squash, make sure to thoroughly drain the liquid. Otherwise, your meal will be soggy. After draining them in a colander, wrap the strands of squash in a dish towel and squeeze out any excess liquid. Works like a charm!

Cauliflower & Cashew
COLESLAW

START TO FINISH: 15 MINUTES
SERVINGS: 5–6

about 1 ½ cups per serving

½ cup plain nonfat Greek yogurt

¼ cup organic mayo (I love Primal's Avocado Oil mayo)

2 Tbsp. apple cider vinegar

½ Tbsp. honey

½ red onion, grated or diced

1 cup fresh grapes, halved, or ½ cup no-sugar-added golden raisins

Pinch of salt to taste

½ cup sunflower seeds

1 head of cauliflower, hard center removed and cut into bite-sized pieces

¼ cup green onion, sliced

½ cup cashews, roughly chopped

MACROS/SERVING

Calories: 342

Protein: 10.9g

Total Fat: 25.8g

Saturated Fat: 3.8g

Carbs: 22.1g

Sugars: 6.1g

Fiber: 5.7g

If you love coleslaw, but hate its high amount of saturated fat, you will love this recipe! Using plain nonfat Greek yogurt mixed with organic mayo keeps the authentic taste of coleslaw without the added fat and cholesterol. Tossing in cashews, or any nut you love, gives this recipe a dash of saltiness which pairs perfectly with the sweet grapes. Talk about a party in your mouth.

Keep in mind… This recipe makes a lot! So if you don't plan on feeding your friends, family, and/or coworkers, you may want to cut this recipe in half or use half of a head of cauliflower.

WHISK together the plain nonfat Greek yogurt, mayo, vinegar, and honey in a medium-sized bowl. Add the red onion, grapes or raisins, and salt. Mix it well. Let the ingredients set while you prep the cauliflower, if this has not been done already.

ADD the cashews, sunflower seeds, cauliflower, and green onion to the bowl. Toss them together.

TOP the mixture with a few more sliced green onions if desired. Serve it immediately or store it in an airtight container in the fridge for up to one week.

Grilled Mediterranean
QUINOA SALAD

START TO FINISH: 20 MINUTES
SERVINGS: 4

1 ½ cups per serving

1 lb. chicken breasts

1 cup quinoa, cooked

1 pint cherry tomatoes, halved

1 green pepper, diced

½ medium red onion, diced

1 cucumber, seeds removed and diced

¼ cup feta cheese

2 Tbsp. olive oil

1 lemon, juiced

1 tsp. oregano

1–2 Tbsp. fresh parsley

Salt and pepper to taste

MACROS/SERVING

Calories: 314

Protein: 28.9g

Total Fat: 12.2g

Saturated Fat: 3.1g

Carbs: 22.1g

Sugars: 3.4g

Fiber: 3.4g

PRO TIP:

If you're really short on time, use a seedless cucumber. They taste great, save time, and eliminate the mess.

Mediterranean food is one of my favorites. After travelling to Greece, I can't deny the tastiness of real feta cheese soaked in brine and served covered in olive oil. Seriously, it's to die for. If you're going to splurge on one item, make it authentic feta cheese. It tastes substantially better, and is well worth the investment. You can find authentic feta cheese soaked in brine at international grocery stores, and most specialty food markets, such as Whole Foods.

This salad is a tribute to the real "Greek salad" (real Greek salads do not contain lettuce or leafy greens), with the addition of grilled chicken and quinoa to make this dish more substantial. Sprinkle the salad with fresh parsley and oregano, and enjoy!

LIGHTLY coat the chicken with salt and pepper. Grill it for 5–6 mins per side, or until the chicken reaches an internal temperature of 160–185°F. If you don't have a grill, cook the chicken in a skillet on the stove over medium heat for 8–12 minutes, turning occasionally.

COMBINE all the diced ingredients in a medium-sized bowl with quinoa, lemon juice, olive oil, oregano, parsley, salt, and pepper.

CUT the chicken into bite-sized pieces. Combine it with ingredients in the bowl. Mix them well and serve it cold. Store the leftovers in an airtight container in the fridge for up to one week.

Ground Turkey
BURRITO BOWLS

START TO FINISH: **20 MINUTES**
SERVINGS: **4**

¼ cup cooked rice
+ 1 ½ cup meat mixture
+ ¼ avocado per serving

1 Tbsp. olive oil

1 lb. lean ground turkey

1 green pepper, diced

1 small red onion, diced

2 garlic cloves, minced

1 ½ tsp. chili powder

1 ½ tsp. cumin

Salt and pepper to taste

½ cup dry, quick-cooking brown rice

2 limes, juiced

1 can black beans, drained

4 Tbsp. fresh cilantro, chopped

1 avocado, sliced

Fresh salsa for topping

MACROS/SERVING

Calories: 428

Protein: 33.2g

Total Fat: 19g

Saturated Fat: 4.1g

Carbs: 34.3g

Sugars: 0.6g

Fiber: 13.3g

This recipe is my version of Chipotle's infamous Ground Beef Burrito Bowl. Taking the time to prepare the rice with lime, cilantro, and salt is the key to making this recipe taste like the original.

We're using ground turkey instead of ground beef to cut down the fat. You may also notice that cheese and sour cream are not included. This is correct. Instead, avocado is this dish's one, not three (typically served with artery-clogging full-fat sour cream, cheese, AND avocado), source of healthy fat. Have some extra time? Serve it with fresh guacamole.

My recommendation: Make a double batch and freeze half of it in individual serving size containers. On days where you open the fridge and hear crickets, pop this in the microwave for 3 minutes and enjoy.

COOK the rice according to the directions. Add the juice of 1 lime, 1 Tbsp. cilantro, and a pinch of salt to the rice.

HEAT the oil in a large sauté pan over medium-high heat. Add the diced green pepper, red onion, garlic, salt, and pepper. Cook these ingredients until soft or about 2–3 minutes.

ADD the ground turkey, chili powder, and cumin to the pan. Cook the turkey until browned or about 4–5 minutes.

ADD the black beans and the rest of the cilantro. Let everything simmer for 2 minutes until the beans are heated through.

SERVE the ground turkey mixture over ¼ cup of the cooked rice. Top with ¼ of the avocado, cilantro, and fresh salsa.

FRESH GUAC

COMBINE 1 avocado with ¼ cup red onion; 1 lime, juiced; 2 Tbsp. cilantro; and salt.

¼ of the guacamole = 1 serving

GRILLED BBQ PORK CHOPS
with Mango Salsa

START TO FINISH: **15 MINUTES**
SERVINGS: **2**

1 pork chop + 2 cups of spinach + ½ cup mango salsa per serving

2 center-cut pork chops, 4oz. each

⅓ cup natural BBQ sauce (I love Trader Joe's Carolina BBQ Sauce)

2 cloves garlic, minced

Salt and pepper to taste

4 cups of spinach

Serve with ½ cup mango salsa from page 102

MACROS/SERVING

Calories: 404

Protein: 24.4g

Total Fat: 19.7g

Saturated Fat: 5.1g

Carbs: 40.6g

Sugars: 29.2g

Fiber: 6.1g

Pork is not something I often eat. When I do, this is my go-to recipe. All you need are pork chops, BBQ sauce, mango salsa, and a pan. It doesn't get much simpler than that. The tanginess of the BBQ sauce pairs perfectly with the sweetness of the mango salsa. It's a match made in heaven. If you don't eat pork, this recipe also tastes great with grilled chicken or any white fish.

PREHEAT the grill to medium-high heat. Combine the BBQ sauce, garlic, salt, and pepper in a small bowl. Coat the pork chops with the sauce, leaving a little left for brushing the pork when it is on the grill. If you don't have a grill, cook the pork chops over the stove on medium heat in a pan for 8–10 minutes, flipping halfway.

GRILL the pork chops for 3–4 minutes per side, or until it reaches an internal temperature of 145°F.

MAKE the mango salsa while the pork chops are cooking (see page 102).

SERVE the pork chops over 2 cups of spinach. Top each pork chop with ½ cup of the mango salsa.

Apple Bacon
HARVEST SALAD

START TO FINISH: 10 MINUTES
SERVINGS: 1

2 cups of mixed greens

⅓ cup quinoa, cooked

½ medium-large apple, sliced thin

2 slices of nitrate-free, uncured bacon

1 oz. or 1 small handful of slivered almonds or walnuts

1 Tbsp. apple cider vinegar

½ Tbsp. olive oil

MACROS/SERVING

Calories: 455

Protein: 17.8g

Total Fat: 29g

Saturated Fat: 4.3g

Carbs: 37g

Sugars: 8.5g

Fiber: 8.5g

I love making this salad in fall when apples are in season. The sweetness of the apple pairs perfectly with the savory saltiness of the bacon. Tossing in a few nuts gives this dish a satisfying crunch while adding extra protein. If you're vegetarian, leave out the bacon and add 1–2 hard-boiled eggs.

COOK the bacon slices in a skillet over medium heat until they're crispy, or about 5 minutes, turning them halfway through. Set them on a paper towel to cool. Once cooled, break them into pieces and set them aside.

COMBINE the olive oil and apple cider vinegar in a small bowl. Set the bowl aside.

LAYER the mixed greens, cooked quinoa, apple slices, bacon, and nuts in a medium-sized bowl or large plate. Top this with dressing and eat it immediately.

PRO TIP:
Make this recipe even faster by preparing the bacon in advance.

CAJUN FISH TACOS
with Spicy Crema

START TO FINISH: **25 MINUTES**
SERVINGS: **4**

> 2 tacos + ¼ avocado
> + 1 Tbsp. spicy crema
> + ½ cup slaw per serving

SLAW

2 cups broccoli slaw

½ red onion, chopped

4 Tbsp. cilantro, chopped

1 lime, juiced

Salt and pepper to taste

SPICY CREMA

¼ cup plain nonfat Greek yogurt

1–2 Tbsp. hot sauce, depending on how spicy you like it

Pinch of salt

TACOS

1 lb. white fish (cod, mahi mahi, tilapia)

2 Tbsp. olive oil

½ lime, juiced

1–2 garlic clove(s), minced

1 tsp. Cumin

2 tsp. Paprika

½ tsp. red chili powder or cayenne pepper

Salt and pepper to taste

8 soft corn tortillas

1 avocado, sliced

These fish tacos are a must-have dinner at least once a month. They're TACOS. Need I say more? Not only are these ingredients amazing together, but they're great served separately. The spicy crema is the perfect lower-calorie replacement for sour cream and tastes great with chili and soup. The broccoli slaw is delicious served over ground turkey or chicken, or alone as a salad. Combined into tacos, this makes for one knock-out recipe.

My recommendation: For even more crunch, add sliced radishes!

PREHEAT the oven to high broiler.

COMBINE the olive oil, lime juice, cumin, red chili powder, garlic, paprika, salt, and pepper in a small bowl. Dip the fish into the bowl until evenly coated with the marinade. Place the fish onto a baking pan or tray and let it marinate in the refrigerator for 5–10 minutes.

WHISK together all the crema ingredients. Set the mixture aside.

COMBINE all the slaw ingredients in a large bowl. Set the mixture aside.

BROIL the fish for 9–10 minutes until the fish is flaky when touched with a fork. Transfer the fish onto a plate and break the fish into small pieces using a fork.

HEAT the corn tortillas in a pan over the stove for a few seconds.

DIVIDE the fish evenly among the corn tortillas. Top two corn tortillas with ¼ cup of the slaw mixture, ¼ of the avocado, and 1 Tbsp. of the crema. Eat them immediately, or store the ingredients separately in an airtight container in the fridge for up to one week.

MACROS/SERVING

Calories: 402
Protein: 29.5g
Total Fat: 14.0g
Saturated Fat: 2.1g
Carbs: 36.4g
Sugars: 1.9g
Fiber: 5.2g

Avocado and Veggie
POWER BOWL

START TO FINISH: 5 MINUTES
SERVINGS: 1

1 cup of spinach

4–5 baby carrots, sliced thin

⅓ cucumber, peeled and sliced

1 handful cherry tomatoes, halved

½ cup of canned black beans, drained and rinsed

¼ avocado, sliced

2 Tbsp. feta cheese

½ lemon, juiced

1 Tbsp. olive oil

Salt and pepper to taste

MACROS/SERVING

Calories: 368

Protein: 11.6g

Total Fat: 23g

Saturated Fat: 3.8g

Carbs: 36.1g

Sugars: 4.2g

Fiber: 14.8g

Power bowls are something I discovered about two years ago. In a nutshell, they're a combination of fresh veggies served with a grain, protein, and/or a healthy fat. They're loaded with nutrition and you should eat them. Feel free to modify this recipe based on the food you have available. No need to run to the store if you don't have feta cheese. Hummus is a great swap, or throw in some sliced olives. This bowl also tastes great served with leftover chicken or fish.

COMBINE the lemon juice and olive oil in a small bowl. Set the mixture aside.

PLACE all of the ingredients in a bowl or on a plate. Top with the lemon juice mixture, salt, and pepper. Eat it immediately.

ONE-PAN LEMON & GARLIC SALMON
with Asparagus

START TO FINISH: 15–20 MINUTES
SERVINGS: 2

2 fillets of wild-caught salmon, approximately 4 oz. each, skin removed

2 garlic cloves, minced

2 Tbsp. fresh parsley, chopped

2 lemons, juiced

1 lemon, sliced to garnish

1 bunch asparagus (24 spears), woody ends removed

Salt and pepper to taste

MACROS/SERVING

Calories: 153

Protein: 21.5g

Total Fat: 2.1g

Saturated Fat: 0.1g

Carbs: 19.8g

Sugars: 1.2g

Fiber: 7.0g

One-pan dishes are a lifesaver when you're in a rush. Throw everything in the pan, stick it in the oven, and forget about it — well, until the timer goes off. Speaking of timing, check the salmon for doneness after five minutes. It should be tender and slightly pink in the middle with a white cream beginning to ooze on top. If the asparagus is not cooked to your liking, take out the salmon and continue cooking the asparagus for a few more minutes. Top it with fresh parsley and dinner is served!

PREHEAT the oven broiler (or grill) to high heat. Line a baking sheet with aluminium foil. Spray it with non-stick spray. Place the broiler pan in the second slot from the top (about 8 inches from the heat element).

COMBINE the lemon juice, garlic, parsley, salt, and pepper in a small bowl. Mix them together.

COAT the salmon with ½ of the lemon juice mixture. Place them on the baking sheet.

TOSS the asparagus with the remaining lemon juice mixture and place the asparagus around the salmon in a single layer. Top the salmon with the fresh lemon slices.

BROIL (or grill; see note below) for 5–8 minutes, or until the salmon starts to "sweat" (a white cream will appear on top).

ARRANGE the salmon and asparagus on individual plates and top them with extra parsley if desired.

NOTES:

If this is being made on the grill, wrap the salmon and asparagus in aluminum foil. Grill the salmon and asparagus on high heat for 5–8 minutes, or until the salmon starts to sweat and the asparagus is tender. Don't like asparagus? This recipe also tastes great with green beans or brussel sprouts!

Asian Lettuce WRAPS

START TO FINISH: **15-20 MINUTES**

SERVINGS: **4**

> 3 wraps per serving,
> 12 wraps total

1 lb. 95% or higher lean ground beef (I prefer grass-fed)

1 Tbsp. sesame oil or olive oil

½ red onion, chopped

2 cloves garlic, minced

1-inch ginger root, grated into the pan (it can also be minced)

4 Tbsp. hoisin sauce

1 Tbsp. gluten-free soy sauce

12 leafs of lettuce

1 cup shredded carrots

¼ cup roughly chopped peanuts

½ cup green onion, chopped

1 avocado, sliced

MACROS/SERVING

Calories: 369

Protein: 28.1g

Total Fat: 21.6g

Saturated Fat: 5.2g

Carbs: 17.7g

Sugars: 3.0g

Fiber: 5.1g

The first time I made these wraps, I was desperately craving saucy, artery-clogging Chinese takeout. Thankfully for my arteries, I made these wraps instead. Hoisin sauce makes this dish taste authentic, so don't skip it if you have it available. Hoisin sauce can be found in the international foods aisle in most large grocery stores. It will look like jelly in a little glass bottle. Don't eat red meat? Use ground turkey instead.

HEAT 1 Tbsp. of oil in a large pan over medium heat. Cook the red onion, garlic, and ginger for 3–4 minutes.

ADD the ground beef. Season it with salt and pepper and cook it until it is no longer pink or 5–7 minutes.

DRAIN the meat. Stir in the hoisin sauce and soy sauce. Cook it for 2–3 minutes.

DIVIDE the ground beef between lettuce leafs, about ½ cup of beef each. Top each serving of wraps with 1 pinch of shredded carrots, 1 Tbsp. of peanuts, 1 pinch of green onion, ¼ avocado, and extra hoisin sauce if desired.

Turkey Kielbasa, Peppers, &
SWEET POTATO HASH

START TO FINISH: 25 MINUTES
SERVINGS: 4

About 1 ½ cups per serving
+ 1 Tbsp. parmesan cheese

2 Tbsp. olive oil

3 medium-sized sweet potatoes, cubed

14 oz. fully-cooked turkey kielbasa, cut into ¼-inch rounds

1 yellow onion, thinly sliced

2 bell peppers, thinly sliced

½ tsp. chili powder

¼ cup freshly-grated parmesan cheese

Salt and pepper to taste

MACROS/SERVING

Calories: 355

Protein: 19.8g

Total Fat: 17.7g

Saturated Fat: 2.0g

Carbs: 31.8g

Sugars: 2.8g

Fiber: 5.9g

Turkey kielbasa was a staple in my fridge during college. Not only is it tasty, but it's cheap! It's also pre-cooked, which automatically makes it a win. I love pairing it with sweet potatoes and peppers... and a little bit of parmesan cheese. Eek, I know, cheese equals fat. But sometimes you have to live a little, and that means eating some tasty cheese.

HEAT 1 Tbsp. of olive oil over medium heat in a large skillet. Add the sweet potatoes and season them with salt, pepper, and chili powder. Cover the skillet and cook the sweet potatoes until they are tender (about 10 minutes), stirring occasionally.

ADD the remaining olive oil, onion slices, and pepper. Cook the ingredients, stirring frequently, until the onion slices are soft and translucent and the peppers are tender (about 4 minutes). Season the ingredients with salt and pepper.

ADD the turkey kielbasa and cook it for 2–3 minutes, stirring occasionally, until it is lightly browned and heated through.

PORTION into 1 ½ cup servings, top with 1 Tbsp. parmesan cheese, and eat it immediately.

NOTES:

When you are cooking, if the sweet potatoes are sticking to the pan, add ¼ cup of water and continue cooking them with the lid on the pan.

Ground Turkey Stuffed
ACORN SQUASH

START TO FINISH: 25 MINUTES
SERVINGS: 2

½ acorn squash + ½ ground turkey mixture + 1 Tbsp. parmesan cheese per serving

1 acorn squash

1 Tbsp. olive oil

½ yellow onion, chopped

2 garlic cloves, minced

2 cups mushrooms, sliced

½ lb. lean ground turkey

2 tsp. curry powder

Salt and pepper to taste

2 cups spinach

2 Tbsp. freshly grated parmesan cheese

MACROS/SERVING

Calories: 329

Protein: 33.0g

Total Fat: 10.9g

Saturated Fat: 2.5g

Carbs: 29.8g

Sugars: 2.1g

Fiber: 5.7g

When I first saw an acorn squash, I thought, "How the heck do I eat this thing?!" Fortunately, my roommate at the time showed me how to cook this awkwardly-shaped veggie like a pro. I've experimented with dozens of flavor combinations, but my favorite is curry-seasoned ground turkey topped with a dash of freshly-grated parmesan cheese. Bon appetit!

CUT the top off of the squash. Cut the squash in half, lengthwise. Scoop out the seeds with a spoon.

MICROWAVE the squash on a plate, face-down, for 7–8 minutes, or until you can easily pierce it with a fork.

HEAT the olive oil in a skillet over medium heat. Add the onion, garlic, and mushrooms. Sauté the ingredients for 3 minutes. Add the ground turkey, curry powder, salt, and pepper; cooking the ingredients until the turkey is browned or for about 10 minutes.

ADD the spinach and cook until it's wilted, or for about 1 minute.

SCOOP ½ of the ground turkey filling into the squash halves and top with 1 Tbsp. parmesan cheese.

PESTO CHICKEN
with Tomatoes and Artichoke Hearts

START TO FINISH: 25 MINUTES
SERVINGS: 4

¼ pound chicken (or 1 chicken breast) + 2 cups mixed greens per serving

1 lb. boneless skinless chicken breasts; about 4 chicken breasts

1 14 oz. can artichoke hearts, drained and quartered

1 large tomato, sliced

¼ cup natural basil pesto (1 Tbsp. per serving of chicken)

16–20 basil leafs

1 bag of mixed greens

MACROS/SERVING

Calories: 289

Protein: 25.1g

Total Fat: 16.6g

Saturated Fat: 1.4g

Carbs: 13.6g

Sugars: 0.2g

Fiber: 1.3g

Oh, this recipe— where do I start? Besides it tasting like Italy in your mouth, it's one of the easiest recipes to make in this book. Stack a bunch of veggies on top of chicken and stick it in the oven. How much easier can it get? It doesn't hurt that pesto is involved. Pesto is one of those foods that makes anything it touches taste amazing. So load it on, in moderation of course, and enjoy your Italian masterpiece over a bed of leafy greens.

HEAT the oven to 375°F.

LINE a baking dish with aluminium foil and spray it with non-stick spray. Place the chicken in the pan.

SPREAD the basil pesto over the chicken (1 Tbsp. per serving of chicken). Layer the chicken with basil, tomatoes, and artichoke hearts.

BAKE the ingredients for 20–25 minutes, or until the chicken reaches 160–165°F.

SERVE it over 2 cups of mixed greens.

Maple-Roasted Kale and Chickpea
SWEET POTATO MASH

START TO FINISH: **30 MINUTES**
SERVINGS: **4**

¼ sweet potato mixture +
¼ chickpea, kale, and onion
mixture per serving

1 15-oz. can chickpeas, rinsed and thoroughly dried

½ large yellow onion, cut into 4 wedges

2 Tbsp. olive oil

1 Tbsp. pure maple syrup

2 Tbsp. chopped sage leaves (thyme or rosemary can also be used)

Salt and pepper to taste

2 medium-sized sweet potatoes

1 bunch of kale, stems removed and chopped into 2-inch pieces

MACROS/SERVING

Calories: 298

Protein: 8.9g

Total Fat: 8.7g

Saturated Fat: 1.2g

Carbs: 48.8g

Sugars: 1.1g

Fiber: 8.9g

This recipe pretty much screams "Eat me. I'll make you feel better." This recipe combines warm mashed sweet potatoes with maple syrup topped with crunchy chickpeas and kale. It's the perfect combo for healthy comfort food. In case you're wondering, we just made healthy comfort food a thing. Besides the comfort part, this dish provides you with a dose of fiber, vitamin A, and vitamin C. Talk about a powerhouse dish. Sage (or thyme/rosemary) adds massive amounts of flavor to this dish, so don't skip it! Fresh sage costs less than $5 and can be bought dried as well.

My recommendation: Make a double batch of roasted chickpeas and eat them later as a tasty snack!

PREHEAT the oven to 400°F and line a large baking sheet with aluminum foil or parchment paper.

COMBINE olive oil, maple syrup, and the chopped sage in a small bowl. Mix the ingredients well and set them aside.

ADD the chickpeas and onion wedges to the baking sheet. Coat them with ½ of the syrup and olive oil mixture and season them with salt and pepper.

ROAST the ingredients until the chickpeas are browned and crispy and the onions are soft, or about 20 minutes. While the chickpeas roast, prepare the sweet potatoes.

POKE both sweet potatoes all over with a fork. Cover them with a damp paper towel and microwave them on high for 7 minutes until they are soft.

ONCE they are cooled, peel the skin off of the sweet potatoes with your hands. Put the peeled sweet potatoes into the remaining olive oil and maple syrup mixture and coat them evenly. Season them with salt and pepper and mash them together with a potato masher or fork.

TOSS the kale onto the baking sheet over the chickpea and onion mixture. Season the ingredients again with salt and pepper and cook them until the kale starts to wilt, or about 5 minutes.

DIVIDE the sweet potato mixture between two plates and top it with the chickpea-kale mixture. Serve it immediately.

NOTES:

Make sure your chickpeas and onions are tossed well with the olive oil/maple syrup/sage mixture before they go into the oven. This will help the chickpeas caramelize. Due to the high temperature, keep the onion wedges together when baking to avoid shriveling. When you add the kale, it's ok if the baking sheet is really crowded. It will still cook great!

Homemade
TOMATO BASIL SOUP

START TO FINISH: 5 MINUTES
SERVINGS: 4

> 1 ½ cups per serving + 1 slice of gluten-free bread (optional)

8–10 roma tomatoes

8–10 basil leaves

3 cloves of garlic

3 Tbsp. olive oil

1 yellow onion, quartered

Salt and pepper to taste

4 slices of gluten-free bread for serving (optional)

MACROS/SERVING

Calories: 175

Protein: 2.4g

Total Fat: 12.1g

Saturated Fat: 1.4g

Carbs: 17.5g

Sugars: 13.3g

Fiber: 2.6g

This fresh tomato basil soup trumps its pre-made canned version any day of the week. With five ingredients and a high-powered blender, this soup is ready to go in less time than it takes to pop its pre-made version in the microwave. In the summer, serve this dish cold like gazpacho. In the winter, serve this dish warm with a slice of gluten-free bread. Mmm, mmm, good!™

My recommendation: Make a double batch and store half of it in individual storage containers in the freezer. It has the convenience of canned soup without the sodium overload and processed junk.

BLEND all of the ingredients in a food processor or blender until the mixture is smooth and creamy.

SERVE it hot or cold. If served hot, heat it on the stove over medium-high heat for 5–10 minutes. Enjoy it with one slice of gluten-free bread and top it with fresh basil if desired.

NOTES:

If you don't have a large food processor or blender, you may need to make this recipe in two batches.

Cauliflower
FRIED RICE

START TO FINISH: 30 MINUTES
SERVINGS: 3

1 ½ cups per serving

½ large head of cauliflower

½ cup frozen peas

½ cup frozen corn

½ cup orange peppers or carrots, diced

½ yellow onion, diced

2 garlic cloves, minced

3 eggs, whisked

1 Tbsp. sesame oil or olive oil

Salt and pepper to taste

2 Tbsp. low-sodium, gluten-free, soy sauce

MACROS/SERVING

Calories: 221

Protein: 13.0g

Total Fat: 9.9g

Saturated Fat: 2.3g

Carbs: 21.7g

Sugars: 3.5g

Fiber: 6.0g

Cauliflower is one of the most versatile veggies on this planet, so much so that you can even transform its florets into a low-carb version of rice! I love this recipe for many reasons, but most importantly because it tricks you into eating your veggies while still satisfying your carb cravings. Peppers, peas, onions, and carrots are just some of my favorites to throw in. This recipe can be made with whatever veggies you have available, so get creative and make this dish your own. Need an extra boost of protein? Add shrimp, chicken, or tofu!

My recommendation: Store leftover rice in individual servings (2 cups per bag) in the freezer. Thaw it one day in advance and use it as a replacement for rice in almost any recipe.

CHOP the cauliflower head into big chunks, removing the hard inner core from each section. Place the chopped cauliflower into a food processor. Pulse the chopped cauliflower until the florets are small and look like rice.

HEAT the oil in a wok or large nonstick skillet over medium-high heat. Add the cauliflower, onions, and vegetables and stir-fry them until the cauliflower begins to turn tender, or 3–4 minutes.

ADD the garlic, season the ingredients with salt and pepper, and continue to stir-fry them until the garlic is fragrant, or about 1 minute.

PUSH the mixture to the sides of the pan to create an opening in the center; add the eggs and scramble them. Toss the mixture until it is combined and drizzle in the soy sauce. Mix it again until it is combined. Serve it hot.

Ahi Tuna
POKE BOWL

START TO FINISH: 15–20 MINUTES
SERVINGS: 2

½ cup rice + ½ tuna steak mixture + ½ avocado slices per serving

1 cup brown rice, cooked

2 ahi tuna steaks, wild-caught and sushi-grade

1 ½ Tbsp. gluten-free soy sauce

1 tsp. honey

1 tsp. sesame oil or light olive oil

½ tsp. wasabi paste

¼ cup green onions, chopped (green and white ends)

½ avocado, sliced

½ bunch of radishes, sliced

½ cup sprouts (alfalfa, broccoli or bean)

Pinch of furikake (optional)

MACROS/SERVING

Calories: 379

Protein: 30.1g

Total Fat: 10.9g

Saturated Fat: 1.3g

Carbs: 39.2g

Sugars: 2.9g

Fiber: 4.2g

You're probably reading this title thinking, "WTF is a Poke Bowl?" Well, it's only the Asian version of a Chipotle burrito bowl, no big deal. But really, it is a BIG deal, and it tastes DAMN good. In my opinion, sushi-grade ahi tuna steak is better than sirloin steak right from the farm. I know what you're thinking, "Won't raw fish make me sick?!" If you buy sushi-grade fish and eat it the right way, raw fish is safe and out-of-this-world amazing. Buy it fresh and eat it within three days. Buy it frozen, thaw it, and eat it within three days. There you go, that's how to eat raw tuna and not spend the next two days in the bathroom.

Back to why this recipe is so great. Besides the tuna melting in your mouth, the other ingredients pack an enormous amount of flavor. Unless you really love wasabi, stick to ½ of a teaspoon to avoid an eye-watering kick at the end of your bite. A little goes a long way.

CUT the ahi tuna steaks into ¼ – ⅓-inch cubes.

PLACE the cubes into a bowl and add the soy sauce, honey, oil, and wasabi paste. Toss them well until they are coated. Stir in the chopped green onions.

SCOOP ½ cup of the rice into two bowls. Place the ahi tuna mixture next to the rice and arrange the sprouts and sliced radishes around the rice.

TOP each bowl with ½ of the avocado slices and sprinkle them with furikake if desired. Serve the dish cold.

NOTES:

When buying ahi tuna, look for "wild-caught" and "previously frozen" fillets. Consume raw tuna within 3 days, max, and keep in the refrigerator to avoid getting sick.

Apple Pecan Greek Yogurt
CHICKEN SALAD
(NOT LIKE MAMA USED TO MAKE)

START TO FINISH: 20 MINUTES
SERVINGS: 4

2 lettuce wraps + ¾–1 cup of chicken salad per serving

1 lb. boneless skinless chicken breasts, cut into quarters

2 cups reduced-sodium chicken broth

2–3 dried bay leaves

1 large golden delicious, gala, or fuji apple; chopped small

⅓ cup chopped pecans, walnuts, or almonds

¼ cup red onion, diced

½ cup plain nonfat Greek yogurt

¼ cup organic mayo

1 Tbsp. apple cider vinegar

1 tsp. dijon mustard

Salt and pepper to taste

8 leafs of lettuce, for serving

MACROS/SERVING

Calories: 362

Protein: 30.2g

Total Fat: 22.1g

Saturated Fat: 4.1g

Carbs: 10.6g

Sugars: 6.8g

Fiber: 3.3g

Remember when your mom would make chicken salad as a kid? I never enjoyed this as a child, but instead became obsessed with eating it in college, after learning one secret trick...

Two words: boiled chicken. I was blown away when I first watched my friend Ashley make it this way. I thought for sure she was making a mistake, but nope, she was definitely onto something. Boiling chicken, as weird as it sounds, creates the juiciest chicken ever, making it perfect for shredding into delicious chicken salad.

Pretty, pretty please, I'm begging you; boil the chicken with chicken broth and bay leaves. If you don't, it will taste average, and we're going for fan-freaking-tastic!

Eat this salad in lettuce wraps, over a bed of fresh greens with carrots or celery; seriously, the sky's the limit. It tastes good with pretty much everything, so go wild!

PLACE the chicken into a large pot with the bay leaves and cover it with chicken broth. The chicken should be covered by 1–2 inches of broth.

BOIL the chicken over medium-high heat until it begins to simmer, and bubbles form along the outside of the chicken. Once it is done simmering, turn the heat down to medium and cook the chicken for 12–15 minutes until it's no longer pink and its internal temperature is 160°F.

MIX together the plain nonfat Greek yogurt, mayo, apple cider vinegar, mustard, salt, and pepper in a small bowl. Set the bowl aside.

DRAIN the chicken and transfer it to a medium-sized bowl. Once the chicken cools, shred it using two forks. Add the apples and nuts. Mix them well.

POUR the yogurt mixture over the chicken, then toss it until it is evenly coated. Divide 1 cup of chicken salad. between two lettuce wraps. Serve the dish cold.

Guilt-Free
NACHOS

START TO FINISH: 5 MINUTES
SERVINGS: 1

2 handfuls organic corn tortilla chips (1 serving is roughly 14 chips)

½ cup low-sodium black beans, drained

2 Tbsp. red onion, diced

¼ avocado, sliced

½ lime, juiced

2 Tbsp. fresh cilantro

Fresh salsa for topping

MACROS/SERVING

Calories: 355

Protein: 10.2g

Total Fat: 15.2g

Saturated Fat: 1.4g

Carbs: 50.1g

Sugars: 6.5g

Fiber: 13.4g

You've probably rarely seen the word "guilt-free" before the word "nachos," but I just made that a real thing. You're welcome. This version of nachos cuts out the cheese and sour cream so you can guiltlessly enjoy every bite. If you like your nachos with a kick, throw on a few sliced jalapeños, and if you MUST have something creamy on top, add a dollop of fresh guacamole (recipe on page 122) or spicy crema (recipe on page 128).

PLACE the beans in a microwave safe dish. Microwave for 30–45 seconds until they are warm.

PLACE the corn tortilla chips on a plate or in a dish. Layer them with beans, avocado, onion, salsa, and cilantro. Eat immediately.

CHICKEN THAI CURRY
with Basmati Rice

START TO FINISH: **30 MINUTES**
SERVINGS: **4**

1 ½ cups of coconut thai curry + ¼ cup rice per serving

1 lb. boneless skinless chicken breasts, chopped into 1-inch pieces and seasoned with salt and pepper

1 ½ Tbsp. coconut oil, divided

2 zucchini, cut into ½ inch x 2 inch spears

1 red bell pepper, ribs and seeds removed, sliced

½ yellow onion, sliced

1 Tbsp. fresh ginger, grated or minced

2 cloves of garlic, grated or minced

2 Tbsp. red thai curry paste

1 16-oz. can coconut cream (light coconut milk)

Salt and pepper to taste

1 cup brown basmati rice, cooked

4 Tbsp. cilantro, chopped for topping

Red pepper flakes for garnish if you like it spicy

MACROS/SERVING

Calories: 400

Protein: 29.6g

Total Fat: 19.8g

Saturated Fat: 12.9g

Carbs: 27.3g

Sugars: 3.6g

Fiber: 3.1g

There's something about garlic and ginger soaked in coconut milk that's simply irresistible. Toss in some veggies, curry paste, protein, and cilantro, and you have a recipe that will knock your socks off. By the way, that's a good thing.

In Thailand, I learned a thing or two about cooking with curry paste. The most important step is letting the curry paste "sweat" for 1–2 minutes when you add it into the pan. In other words, stir it around for a few minutes until it becomes fragrant. This releases its flavors, which makes for an unbelievably tasty dish. So don't get impatient and skip this step. One or two minutes can transform this dish from good to great.

HEAT a wok or large skillet over medium-high heat. Add 1 Tbsp. of the coconut oil and cook the chicken until it is golden brown and cooked through, or about 8 minutes, stirring occasionally. Transfer the cooked chicken to a plate.

MELT ½ Tbsp. of the coconut oil in the same wok or skillet over medium-high heat. Add in the thai curry paste and sauté it until it becomes fragrant, or about 1 minute.

ADD in all the vegetables and season them with salt and pepper. Cook the vegetables until they start to brown slightly on the edges, but are still crisp and tender, or about 6–8 minutes, stirring occasionally.

ADD the garlic and ginger; cook them for 30 seconds until they are fragrant. Add coconut milk and stir it in until it is combined.

ADD the chicken back into the skillet. Cook for 2–3 minutes, or until heated through.

SPOON the coconut chicken thai curry over ¼ cup rice and serve it warm. Top it with cilantro and red pepper flakes if you like it spicy.

DESSERTS

Give up chocolate? Live without dessert? Not in my life, and not in this book. This book is anti-diet, which means there's no need to cut out the sweets. However, these are not your typical sugar-loaded desserts. These desserts are actually good for you, and contain NO processed sugar. Only fruit, honey, agave nectar, pure maple syrup, and Stevia are used to sweeten these treats, and guess what: your tastebuds won't notice a difference. If these desserts can satisfy my insistent sweet tooth, they will definitely satisfy yours too! So eat up! And get ready to indulge without the resulting bulge.

Greek Yogurt
"COOKIE DOUGH"

START TO FINISH: **LESS THAN 5 MINUTES**

SERVINGS: **1**

½ cup plain nonfat Greek yogurt

1 Tbsp. cacao nibs, or dark chocolate chips

1 Tbsp. Chocolate Peanut Butter PB2 Powder, or natural peanut butter

¼ tsp. vanilla extract

1 Stevia packet

MACROS/SERVING

Calories: 152

Protein: 15.5g

Total Fat: 6.6g

Saturated Fat: 3.6g

Carbs: 13.2g

Sugars: 6.6g

Fiber: 5.1g

Raw cookie dough is one of those treats that will never get old. Eat enough of it though, and you will begin to notice some dough-like shapes forming on your thighs. This recipe is no cookie dough, but for having less than half the fat and sugar than regular cookie dough, it's a win. If you haven't heard of PB2 or peanut butter powder, look it up. It's peanut butter without the oil, which removes almost all the fat. Peanut butter is filled with good fats, but if you're watching your fat intake, peanut butter powder is a great alternative.

My recommendation: When making this recipe, if you can find PB2 (or any peanut butter powder) and don't mind spending a few more dollars, use it. Since PB2 is a powder, it blends more easily with the yogurt, giving this dessert a mousse-like, airy texture. Otherwise, use natural creamy peanut butter, stirring well to blend it with the yogurt.

MIX all ingredients together in a small bowl. Eat it immediately.

Pumpkin Cranberry
GRANOLA COOKIES

START TO FINISH: 25 MINUTES

SERVINGS: 10

1 cookie per serving

¼ cup coconut oil

2 Tbsp. honey

2 cups rolled old-fashioned oats

⅔ cup unsweetened dried cranberries

⅔ cup pumpkin seeds

¼ cup milled flax seed

1 tsp. pumpkin pie spice or mixture of nutmeg and cinnamon

½ tsp. sea salt

½ cup pumpkin puree

2 eggs, beaten

MACROS/SERVING

Calories: 192

Protein: 4.7g

Total Fat: 9.3g

Saturated Fat: 5.2g

Carbs: 24.2g

Sugars: 9.8g

Fiber: 3.8g

If you have even a mild obsession with pumpkin, you're going to love these cookies. First, they are HUGE. So when you see one cookie per serving, it's one big-ass cookie. Second, they're made with pumpkin! And third, they're cookies! These are all great reasons to eat these bad boys up!

The funny thing is, these cookies contain less sugar than the average "healthy" granola bar. What would you rather have: A store-bought granola bar or a big-ass pumpkin cookie? Exactly.

PREHEAT the oven to 325°F. Line a baking sheet with parchment paper or spray it with coconut oil.

WARM the coconut oil and honey in the microwave for 30 seconds.

COMBINE the oats, cranberries, pumpkin seeds, ground flax, pumpkin pie spice, and salt in a large bowl. Add the pumpkin puree, eggs, and warmed coconut oil and honey mixture. Stir these ingredients until fully combined.

DROP ¼-cup-sized scoops of the mixture onto a cookie sheet and flatten them (so that the cookies won't spread while baking). Bake them for about 15–20 minutes until the edges are lightly browned.

COOL the cookies on the baking sheet before moving them into an airtight storage container.

NOTE:

If your mixture is too dry, add 1–2 Tbsp. of milk or water.

Strawberry
"ICE CREAM" SANDWICH

START TO FINISH: LESS THAN 5 MINUTES

SERVINGS: **1**

1 gluten-free graham cracker

¼ cup frozen all-natural whipped topping (I use So Delicious Light Coco whip)

3–4 fresh strawberries, sliced

MACROS/SERVING

Calories: 116

Protein: 0.8g

Total Fat: 4.6g

Saturated Fat: 2.6g

Carbs: 16.8g

Sugars: 9.0g

Fiber: 1.1g

I acquired this recipe from my friend and former roommate, Emily. Knowing my love of sweets, she shared this gem with me one night when I was having an unbearable sugar craving. In less than 5 minutes, I crafted this tasty 116 calorie dessert, my sugar-craving was gone, and I was loving life. This sandwich is no Ben and Jerry's, but it's also not a heart attack on a plate. So the next time you're craving a big tub of ice cream, do your body a favor and make this dessert instead.

SPLIT the graham cracker in half.

SPREAD the whipped topping on one graham cracker. Top with the strawberries.

PLACE the other graham half on top. Eat it immediately.

NOTE:

The So Delicious Coco Whip is the only pre-made whipped topping brand I've found that doesn't have high-fructose corn syrup and that is not loaded with preservatives. It's also naturally lactose-free. You can find it in the freezer aisle in most big-chain grocery stores.

Chocolate Chia Seed
PROTEIN PUDDING

START TO FINISH: 5 MINUTES
ready in 20–30 minutes, or leave in the fridge overnight

SERVINGS: 1

½ scoop of chocolate protein powder (20g of protein per scoop)

2 Tbsp. chia seeds

1 Tbsp. milled flaxseed

½ cup + 1 Tbsp. of unsweetened coconut milk

¼ tsp. cinnamon

MACROS/SERVING

Calories: 266

Protein: 18.8g

Total Fat: 17.5g

Saturated Fat: 3.6g

Carbs: 22.2g

Sugars: 0.5g

Fiber: 16.8g

Oh chia seed pudding, how I love you so. Not to be dramatic, but seriously... I'm obsessed with this stuff. I even brought chocolate protein powder halfway across the world just so I could make this treat. I ate it almost every day. That's how much I love it.

With almost zero sugar, 17 grams of fiber, and 19 grams of protein, it's a dessert-lover's dream. Enjoy this as a late-night treat, as a filling snack, or as a quick breakfast. Anytime is good, so take your pick!

My recommendation: Leave your pudding in the fridge for at least an hour before eating. The longer it sits, the thicker it gets.

ADD all of the ingredients into a medium-sized bowl or resealable container. I like to use glass mason jars.

MIX the ingredients well or shake them up.

REFRIGERATE the mixture for a minimum of 25 minutes. Eat it immediately or keep it in the fridge for up to 5 days. If desired, top it with fresh fruit before serving.

Fresh Mango and Lime
SORBET

START TO FINISH: **LESS THAN 5 MINUTES**

SERVINGS: **1**

1 cup no-sugar-added frozen mango chunks

¼ cup (60 ml) plain nonfat Greek yogurt

2 Stevia packets or 1 Tbsp. natural sweetener of your choice (these will be higher in sugar)

1 Tbsp. fresh lime juice

Freshly grated lime for garnish

MACROS/SERVING

Calories: 141

Protein: 7.2g

Total Fat: 0.1g

Saturated Fat: 0.0g

Carbs: 34.7g

Sugars: 25.5g

Fiber: 4.9g

Sorbet, the healthy way! Made from real fruit and fresh lime juice, this dessert is packed with flavor, and nutrition. On a hot summer day, this treat will call your name. Simply blend and enjoy!

BLEND all of the ingredients together in a food processor or blender until they are creamy, or about 1 minute.

TOP the sorbet with fresh lime zest. Eat it immediately or store it in an airtight container in the freezer.

Chocolate Coconut
MUG CAKE

START TO FINISH: 5 MINUTES

SERVINGS: 1

½ scoop chocolate protein powder (20g of protein per scoop)

½ tsp. baking powder

1 Tbsp. coconut flour

1 Stevia packet, or ½ Tbsp. natural sweetener of your choice (these will be higher in sugar)

1 Tbsp. cocoa powder

1 large egg or ¼ cup liquid egg whites

¼ cup unsweetened vanilla coconut milk

1 Tbsp. cacao nibs or dark chocolate chips

1 Tbsp. unsweetened coconut flakes

MACROS/SERVING

Calories: 365

Protein: 22.6g

Total Fat: 24.6g

Saturated Fat: 15.2g

Carbs: 23.9g

Sugars: 2.2g

Fiber: 15.5g

Chocolate + coconut = heaven. If you didn't already pick up on the fact that I'm "mildly" coconut-obsessed, it's painfully obvious in this recipe. This cake uses coconut milk, coconut flour, and coconut flakes. It doesn't get more coco-nutty than that. The best part is that it's CAKE!!! Yes, you can have your cake and eat it too, in less than 5 minutes to boot. Score.

ADD the protein powder, baking powder, coconut flour, Stevia, and cocoa powder to your favorite mug. Mix the ingredients well with a fork.

ADD the milk and egg (or liquid egg whites) and mix them well with a fork.

MICROWAVE the mug on high for 1 minute and 30 seconds to 2 minutes, until the center looks almost cooked through. Top it with cacao nibs and coconut flakes. Let it sit for a couple of minutes before eating.

NOTE:

Use a 12 oz. or larger straight-sided mug to ensure your cake cooks evenly. If your batter looks too crumbly, add a little more milk.

"PB&J"
Rice Cake

START TO FINISH: **5 MINUTES**

SERVINGS: **1**

1 plain rice cake
1 Tbsp. peanut butter or other nut butter
1 tsp. milled flax seeds
¼ cup fresh blueberries

MACROS/SERVING

Calories: 155
Protein: 5.7g
Total Fat: 7.7g
Saturated Fat: 1.0g
Carbs: 15.8g
Sugars: 4.8g
Fiber: 2.6g

Growing up, my mom would buy those Smuckers Uncrustable Peanut Butter and Jelly Sandwiches by the dozen. On average, my brothers and I would demolish at least two a day, each. Fortunately, we had high metabolisms, and burned through them in about 5 minutes. Fast-forward 15 years later; my metabolism no longer operates like a young thoroughbred horse, yet my love of PB&J sandwiches remains the same. In search of a solution, this recipe was born. Rice cakes contain almost no carbs or calories, and fresh blueberries are loaded with nutrients and are naturally low in sugar. So you can keep eating those beloved PB&J sandwiches, but without the calories and the guilt.

SPREAD the peanut butter onto the rice cake.

TOP the rice cake with fresh blueberries and flax seeds. Eat it immediately.

PRO TIP:

Use milled flax seeds, not whole flax seeds, when making this recipe. Whole flax seeds pass through your body without being digested, which means your body misses out on a lot of their essential nutrients. Your body can more easily absorb the nutrients in flax seeds if they are milled or ground.

Berry

AVOCADO BOWL

START TO FINISH: LESS THAN 5 MINUTES

SERVINGS: 1

1 cup of fresh or frozen berries

½ tsp. honey

½ avocado

½ Tbsp. chia seeds

¼ cup berries for topping

MACROS/SERVING

Calories: 248

Protein: 6.3g

Total Fat: 15.1g

Saturated Fat: 2.3g

Carbs: 30.2g

Sugars: 2.9g

Fiber: 13.8g

I know what you're thinking, "Avocado for dessert? Really?" Yes, really. Surprisingly, this unique combo tastes sinfully delicious. Avocado creates a creamy texture when blended with frozen berries, similar to mouth-watering gelato. Not to mention, avocados are loaded with potassium and fiber (They actually have MORE potassium than bananas!). Eat away, but stick with the ½ avocado serving recommendation due to their high fat and carbohydrate content.

BLEND the berries, honey, and avocado in a food processor or blender. Pour the mixture into a bowl.

TOP it with fresh berries and chia seeds. Eat it immediately.

Flourless Chocolate Chip
CHICKPEA BLONDIES

START TO FINISH: **25 MINUTES**

SERVINGS: **MAKES 9 BLONDIES**

1 per serving

1 15-oz. can chickpeas, rinsed and drained

1 egg

½ cup all-natural peanut butter or almond butter

¼ cup pure maple syrup or natural sweetener of your choice

2 tsp. vanilla extract

½ tsp. salt

¼ tsp. baking powder

¼ tsp. baking soda

¼ cup dark chocolate chips

Sea salt for sprinkling

MACROS/SERVING

Calories: 205

Protein: 6.1g

Total Fat: 10.4g

Saturated Fat: 3.1g

Carbs: 23.1g

Sugars: 10.0g

Fiber: 3.4g

OMG, who knew blondies could be made from chickpeas and taste this good?! Who even knew that you could make a dessert from beans? Well, whoever figured it out, thank you dearly. I swear, you can't tell the difference between these blondies, and ones made from plain, old flour and sugar. They're moist and decadent. I would even compare them to peanut butter chocolate fudge. Every time I sink my teeth into one, it's like I've died and gone to heaven. Don't judge until you try one yourself. I have a feeling you will feel the same.

PREHEAT the oven to 350°F and spray an 8x8-inch pan with nonstick cooking spray.

BLEND all of the ingredients together in a food processor or blender, except chocolate chips, until the batter is smooth. Fold in the dark chocolate chips.

SPREAD the batter evenly in a prepared pan. Bake for 20–25 minutes, or until a toothpick comes out clean and the edges are a tiny bit brown. The batter will look a little underdone.

COOL the pan for 15–20 minutes. Sprinkle the dish with sea salt then cut it into nine squares. Eat it immediately or store it in an airtight container.

COOKING CONVERSION CHARTS

Note: Metric weights listed have been slightly rounded to make measuring easier.

WEIGHT

U.S.	METRIC
¼ oz.	7g
½ oz.	15g
¾ oz.	20g
1 oz.	30g
8 oz. (½ lb.)	225g
12 oz. (¾ lb.)	340g
16 oz. (1 lb.)	455g
2 lb.	900g
2 ¼ lb.	1kg

VOLUME

U.S.	METRIC	IMPERIAL
¼ tsp.	1.2ml	
½ tsp.	2.5ml	
1 tsp.	5ml	
½ Tbsp. (1 ½ tsp.)	7.5ml	
1 Tbsp. (3 tsp.)	15ml	
¼ cup (4 Tbsp.)	60ml	2 fl oz.
⅓ cup (5 Tbsp.)	75ml	2.5 fl oz.
½ cup (8 Tbsp.)	125ml	4 fl oz.
⅔ cup (10 Tbsp.)	150ml	5 fl oz.
¾ cup (12 Tbsp.)	175ml	6 fl oz.
1 cup (16 Tbsp.)	250ml	8 fl oz.
1 ¼ cup	300ml	10 fl oz. (½ pint)
2 cups (1 pint)	350ml	12 fl oz.
2 ½ cups	500ml	16 fl oz.
1 quart	625ml	20 fl oz. (1 pint)
	1 liter	32 fl oz.

OVEN

FAHRENHEIT (°F)	CELSIUS (°C)	GAS MARK	OVEN TERMS
225	110	¼	Very Cool
250	130	½	Very Cool
275	140	1	Very Cool
300–325	150	2	Cool
350	165	3	Cool
375	177	4	Medium
400	190	5	Medium
425	200	6	Medium Hot
450	220	7	Hot
475	230	8	Hot
500	245	9	Hot
525	260	10	Very Hot
550	290	10	Broiling

ACKNOWLEDGMENTS

I don't even know where to begin. This book was a true team effort, and I am so appreciative of everyone who was involved. But since I have to start somewhere, let's begin with who helped create the bare bones of this book. Thank you to my friend Chara for letting me use her beautiful kitchen every weekend to photograph and shoot videos. And thank you for intricately staging each plate that was photographed. You transformed my recipes into delectable works of art.

Thank you to my friend Julie Fisher for spending countless hours photographing each recipe. The pictures are gorgeous, and this book would not be what it is if it wasn't for your amazing photos.

Thank you to Julie Hove Andersen for photographing my kick-ass cover photo and for helping me create videos to promote this book. You perfectly captured my message and vision, and I am so thankful to have been able to work with you.

Thank you to all of my friends including, Erin, Kait, Jenna, Jessie, Kaitlin, Kristin, and Aandria for answering my millions of questions and emails throughout this process, and for being my voice of sanity when I was going crazy. I love each and every one of you, and I cannot express how grateful I am to have you in my life.

Thank you to everyone in my family, especially my Uncle Marty, for being my biggest supporters from the day I entered this world. You continue to show me love and support every day, and I couldn't ask for anything more. I love you all so much!

Thank you to all the editors who contributed to making this book the best version of itself. And thank you to my wonderful designer, Alexa, for bearing with me through my nit-picking and non-stop editing. You did an amazing job!

Lastly, thank YOU for purchasing and reading this book. When you did this, you took a stand toward changing your story, your body, and your life. I thank you for letting me share my experiences with you, and I hope this information helps you live an amazing and thriving life, every day.

INDEX

RECIPE INDEX

ABOUT THE AUTHOR

Katie Sampayo is the founder of katiesampayo.com. She is a personal trainer, yoga instructor, nutrition expert, self-made cook, adventure-seeker, and lover of life. Her mission is to help others live amazing and thriving lives through sharing her knowledge and passion about health, wellness, and nutrition. Katie is looking forward to traveling the world and sharing her mission with as many people as she can. Her goal is to positively impact one million lives, and she is excited for the challenge.

STAY CONNECTED WITH KATIE!

Follow Katie on social media and hashtag #Live2Thrive to share your tasty and healthy bangin, ass meals with her and others in the community. Katie will pick one mouth-watering photo each week to feature on her social media pages! So make sure to use the hashtag and to tag Katie in your posts for your chance to be featured!

www.katiesampayo.com

 facebook.com/ksampayofitness

 @katie_sampayo

 @ksampayo

 @katiesampayo